Success
Assessment Papers

KS3 Maths

LEVELS
5-6

Bob Hartman

paper number for
quick reference

level showing
attainment target

non-calculator
symbol

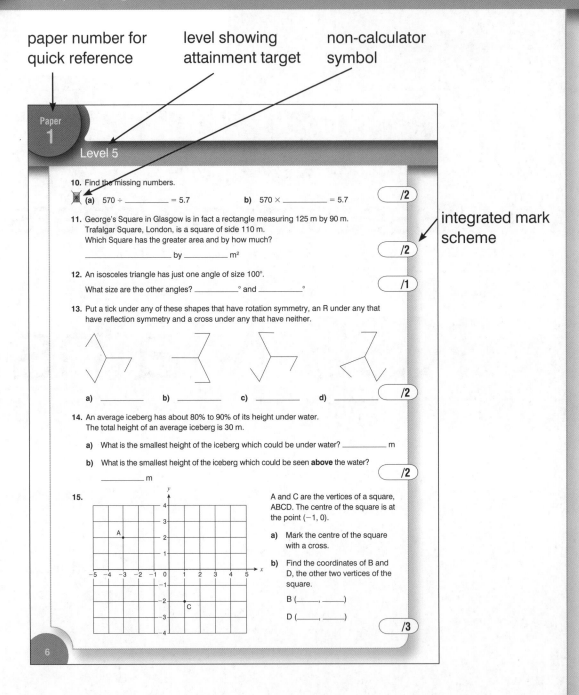

Paper 1

Level 5

integrated mark
scheme

10. Find the missing numbers.

(a) 570 ÷ _____ = 5.7   b) 570 × _____ = 5.7   /2

11. George's Square in Glasgow is in fact a rectangle measuring 125 m by 90 m.
Trafalgar Square, London, is a square of side 110 m.
Which Square has the greater area and by how much?

_____ by _____ m²   /2

12. An isosceles triangle has just one angle of size 100°.

What size are the other angles? _____ ° and _____ °   /1

13. Put a tick under any of these shapes that have rotation symmetry, an R under any that
have reflection symmetry and a cross under any that have neither.

a) _____   b) _____   c) _____   d) _____   /2

14. An average iceberg has about 80% to 90% of its height under water.
The total height of an average iceberg is 30 m.

a) What is the smallest height of the iceberg which could be under water? _____ m

b) What is the smallest height of the iceberg which could be seen **above** the water?

_____ m   /2

15.

A and C are the vertices of a square,
ABCD. The centre of the square is at
the point (−1, 0).

a) Mark the centre of the square
with a cross.

b) Find the coordinates of B and
D, the other two vertices of the
square.

B (_____, _____)

D (_____, _____)   /3

6

Contents

PAPER 1

1. Put as many of these fractions as you can into groups with the same value.

$$\frac{2}{3} \qquad \frac{6}{8} \qquad \frac{21}{28} \qquad \frac{25}{35} \qquad \frac{30}{40} \qquad \frac{8}{12} \qquad \frac{10}{14}$$

/2

2. A tap drip has a volume of 0.25 ml.
   It drips about once every 15 seconds.

   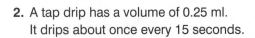
   Don't forget the units

   a) What volume of water a minute is this? _____

   b) How long will it take to fill a 20 litre sink? _____

/4

3. This table shows the different types of mortar needed for different walls.

Type of wall	Ratio of cement to sand in the mortar
Garden wall	1 : 5
House wall	1 : 3
Breeze block	1 : 4

   a) For which sort of wall would these mixtures be suitable:

      (i) 2 shovels of cement with 6 shovels of sand? _House wall_

      (ii) 25 shovels of sand with 5 shovels of cement? _Garden wall_

   b) How many shovels of cement are needed to mix with 20 shovels of sand to

      make mortar for breeze blocks? _5_

/3

4. Here is a set of five numbers: 6 14 4 8 10
   Their mean is 8 and the range is 10.
   The number 8 is added to give a set of six numbers.
   What is the value of the mean and range of this new set of numbers?

   Mean = _____, Range = _____

/2

5. James and Tom went on a jogging machine. James ran 5.07 km and Tom ran 5700 m.
   Who ran further and by how much?

   Tom by _630_ m

/1

6. Estimate the temperature shown on this greenhouse thermometer.

0°   40°

_____25_____ °C   /1

7. Here are the temperatures of five UK cities one day in February.

City	Temperature at midnight	Temperature at midday
Birmingham	2 °C	9 °C
Bristol	3 °C	8 °C
Glasgow	−4 °C	7 °C
London	−2 °C	8 °C
Newcastle	−7 °C	2 °C

a) Which city had the lowest temperature at midnight?

_____Newcastle_____

b) Which city had the greatest temperature rise between midnight and midday?

_____Glasgow_____

c) Which city had the smallest temperature rise between midnight and midday?

_____Bristol_____   /3

8. Using brackets can sometimes help with number sequences.
For example,   7   11   15   ...
is the same as: (1 × 4) + 3   (2 × 4) + 3   (3 × 4) + 3   ...

a) What is term number 100 in the above number sequence? _____403_____

b) Use brackets to help you find term number 1000 in this sequence:

   20   31   42   53   ...   (___×11)+_____   /2

9. Write these in order, with the smallest first.

          10%   0.3 $\frac{15}{100}$ a quarter   7%   0.7

_____7%, 10%, ¹⁵⁄₁₀₀ , a quater, 0.3 , 0.7_____   /1

5

10. Find the missing numbers.

 /2

(a) 570 ÷ ___100___ = 5.7   b) 570 × ___?___ = 5.7

11. George's Square in Glasgow is in fact a rectangle measuring 125 m by 90 m.
Trafalgar Square, London, is a square of side 110 m.
Which Square has the greater area and by how much?

_____ by _____ m²

/2

12. An isosceles triangle has just one angle of size 100°.

What size are the other angles? _____° and _____°

/1

13. Put a tick under any of these shapes that have rotational symmetry, an R under any that
have reflection symmetry and a cross under any that have neither.

 /2

a) _____   b) _____   c) _____   d) _____

/2

14. An average iceberg has about 80% to 90% of its height under water.
The total height of an average iceberg is 30 m.

a) What is the smallest height of the iceberg which could be under water? _____ m

b) What is the smallest height of the iceberg which could be seen **above** the water?

 /2

_____ m

15.

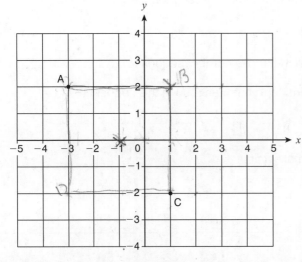

A and C are the vertices of a square,
ABCD. The centre of the square is at
the point (−1, 0).

a) Mark the centre of the square
with a cross.

b) Find the coordinates of B and
D, the other two vertices of the
square.

B (_1_ , _2_)

D (_-3_ , _-2_)

/3

16. Use your calculator to work out the value of:

$$\frac{(4.3 - 0.9)(43.4 + 3.1)}{0.2}$$ _____

/1

17. This is the steepest wheelchair ramp that regulations allow.

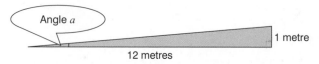

Using a scale of 1 cm to represent 1 m, on a separate piece of paper draw a scale diagram of the ramp and find angle a.

$a =$ _____ °

/1

18. Typing speed is calculated by dividing the number of words typed by the time taken. When r is the typing speed in words per minute, w is the total number of words typed and t is the total time spent typing.

a) Circle any of these formulae that are correct.

$r = w + t \qquad t = r + w \qquad w = \dfrac{r}{t} \qquad r = \dfrac{w}{t} \qquad r = \dfrac{t}{w} \qquad r = wt \qquad t = wr$

b) One of the fastest typists in the world can type 1060 words in 5 minutes.

What typing speed is this? _____ words per minute

/2

19. A fair 10-sided dice numbered from 1 to 10 is thrown.
What is the probability on the next throw:

a) of getting a number of 8 or more? _____

b) of scoring an odd number? _____

c) of getting a 10? _____

/3

20. Solve these equations.

a) $2x = 10 \qquad x =$ _____

b) $x + 6 = 10 \qquad x =$ _____

/2

/40

PAPER 2

1. These marbles are in a bag. One is taken without looking.
   What is the probability that this marble is:

   a) transparent? _____

   b) has a swirly pattern? _____

   c) is not transparent? _____

   /3

2. Draw the lines of symmetry for each of these shapes. Under each shape, write the number of lines of symmetry and the order of rotational symmetry.

   a) Lines of symmetry: _____

   Order of rotational symmetry: _____

   b) Lines of symmetry: _____

   Order of rotational symmetry: _____

   /2

3. Write these in order of size, lightest first.

   $\frac{1}{2}$ kg   2.0 kg   20 kg   2.00 g   0.1 kg   0.01 kg $1\frac{1}{2}$ g

   $1\frac{1}{2}g, 2.00g, 0.01kg, 0.1kg, \frac{1}{2}kg, 2.0kg, 20kg$

   /1

4. To put national Olympic teams in order, a newspaper awards 4 points for gold, 3 for silver and 1 for bronze.

   a) Write the formula for the total number of points, P, gained by a country winning gold, g, silver, s, and bronze, b, medals.

   $P = $ _____

   b) A country gained a total of 8 points using this method.
   List all the different ways they could have gained 8 points.

   _____

   _____

   /3

5. Add brackets so that each of these calculations is correct.

    a) $7 + 2 \times 9 + 6 = 37$ **b)** $7 + 2 \times 9 + 6 = 87$

/2

6. One of the angles, a, of an isosceles triangle, with angles a, b and c, is 40°.
What might be the sizes of angles b and c?

/3

_____

7. These are the average monthly temperatures at the South Pole.

Month	Jan	Feb	Mar	Apr	May	Jun	Jul	Aug	Sep	Oct	Nov	Dec
Temperature (°C)	−27	−40	−53	−56	−57	−58	−59	−59	−59	−50	−38	−28

    a) Which is the warmest month? _____

    b) For how many months is the temperature less than −30 °C? _____

    c) The coldest temperature ever recorded was −89 °C.
         How much colder is this than the coldest month at the South Pole? _____°

/3

8. The shape of TV screens is described by the ratio of their width, w, to their height, h.

There are two different types: $w : h = 4 : 3$ and $w : h = 16 : 9$

Which of these screens are 4 : 3 and which are 16 : 9 screens?

    (i) 36 cm by 27 cm   (ii) 48 cm by 27 cm
    (iii) 32 inches by 24 inches   (iv) 64 inches by 36 inches

    a)   4 : 3   _____

    b)   16 : 9   _____

/2

9. By drawing on a separate piece of paper and
measuring accurately, find the missing side
and angle of this triangle.

$b =$ _____ cm

$a =$ _____ °

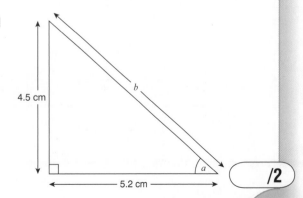

4.5 cm

b

a

5.2 cm

/2

9

10. Here are the results of counting the number of matches in ten new matchboxes.

| 45 | | 42 | | 47 | | 46 | | 41 |
| 49 | | 46 | | 42 | | 48 | | 44 |

a) What is the range of these numbers? _____

b) What should it say on the label about the average contents of the box?

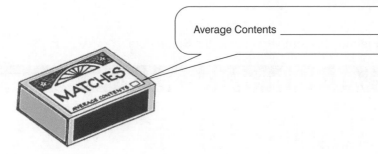

Average Contents _____

/2

11. Amy makes a fraction using two number cards.
Her fraction is equivalent to 25%. One of the number cards is 8.
What could Amy's fraction be? List all the possible answers.

_____

/2

12. ABCD is a rhombus.

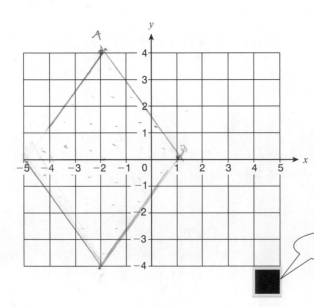

a) Plot the points A(−2, 4), B(1, 0) and C (−2, −4).

b) Find and label point D.

(−5, 0)

c) Find the area of the rhombus. 22−26 cm²

1 cm²

/4

13. A model railway track is made up from three different pieces of track:

long straight sections (45 cm long)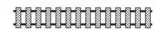

short straight sections (25 cm long)

curved sections (20 cm long)

a) A layout is made from long sections, *l*, short sections, *s*, and curved sections, *c*. Write the formula for the total length, *T*, of the track in centimetres.

$T =$ _____

b) Write an expression for the total length of the track in metres.

_____

/2

14. Solve these equations.

a) $x + 4 = 15$ $x =$ _____

b) $5x + 9 = 29$ $x =$ _____

/2

15.

a) What percentage of these tiles are shaded? Circle the best estimate.

40%   50%   60%   70%   80%

b) What is the ratio of shaded squares to white squares? _____

c) How many more white squares need to be shaded so that the ratio of white to shaded squares is 1 : 3? _____

/3

16. This bar chart shows the number of road accidents in a small county in 2009.

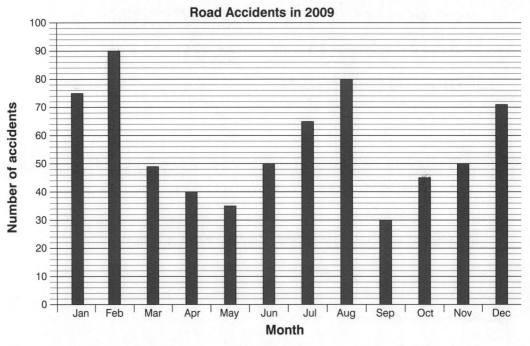

Road Accidents in 2009

a) What was the total number of accidents in 2009? _____

b) In which month were there 50% more accidents than in June? ___January___

c) One month had double the accidents of another.

Which two months were these? ___October___ and ___February___

d) Without working it out, circle the most reasonable value for the mean number of accidents a month in 2009.

40   45   55   65   70   75

/4

/40

PAPER 3

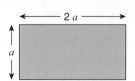

1. The shapes below are made up from rectangular tiles like these.

a) Write down the formula for the perimeter of each of these shapes. (Simplify your formula as much as possible.)

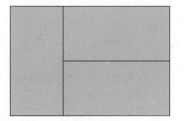

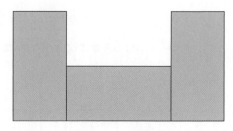

(i) P = _____   (ii) P = _____

b) What is the difference in the size of the perimeter for the two shapes? _____ /3

2. Here is a recipe for dark orange paint: | Mix yellow and red paint in the ratio 2 : 5

a) To make dark orange paint, how many tins of yellow paint should be mixed with 30 tins of red? _____

b) Herman has 20 tins of yellow paint and 20 tins of red paint. How many tins of dark orange could he make? _____ /2

3. Here are five number cards.

  9   29   35   41   59

Two of the cards are taken and the numbers on them multiplied. Which two numbers were they, if the result is:

a) less than 300? _____ and _____

b) between 1000 and 2000 and ends in a 5? (N.B. there may be more than one answer.)

_____ and _____

c) over 2000 and ending in a 9? _____ and _____ /3

4. A square's sides are 1 m in length. What is the area and perimeter of the square in cm² and cm? /2

Area = _____ cm²   Perimeter = _____ cm

5. Here are the handspans, in millimetres, of a group of people.

225	194	216	180	188
194	212	198	205	200
185	198	194		

a) What is the range of the handspans? _____ mm

b) What is the median of the handspans? _____ mm

c) What is the mean of the handspans? _____ mm

/3

6.

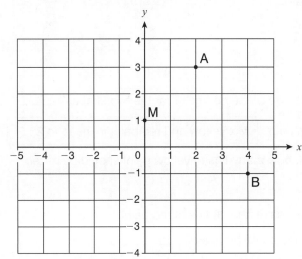

A and B are two corners of a parallelogram.
M is the point where the two diagonals of the parallelogram intersect.

a) Find the coordinates of the other two corners of the parallelogram.

(_____, _____)(_____, _____)

b) Write down the coordinates of the midpoint of the side AB.

(_____, _____)

/3

7. Complete these calculations.

a) $1.5 \times \underline{5} = 7.5$

b) $8.4 \div \underline{2} = 4.2$

c) $(1.6 - 0.3) \div 10 = \underline{0.13}$

d) $(15 \div \underline{5}) + 2 = 5$

/4

8. Pressure increases the deeper you go down into the sea.

$P = 0.1 \times d + 1$ where P is the pressure in atmospheres at a depth of d metres.

a) What is the pressure at a depth of 20 m? _____ atmospheres

b) Deepest parts of the Pacific are 11 km deep.
What is the pressure at this depth? _____ atmospheres

/2

9. Write a decimal that is greater than 75% and less than $\frac{9}{10}$ ___0.8___

/1

10. Which three of these vertices could have come from the same triangle?

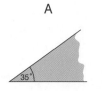 A   B   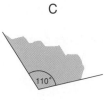 C   D   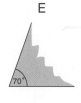 E   F

A 35°   B 75°   C 110°   D 45°   E 70°   F 85°

____*A, B, E*____

/1

11. This van is 8.5 m long.

   a) Estimate:

      (i) the length of the car ___4.25___ m

      (ii) the height of the lamp post.

         ___11.5___ m

   b) The van travels about 20000 miles a year. Fuel costs work out at about 10p a mile. About how much a week will fuel cost?

     ___£38.40___

/3

12.

  A   B   C   D   E

Write the letter of each traffic sign in the correct box.

		Number of lines of reflection symmetry				
		None	1	2	3	4
Rotation	None					
	Order 2					
	Order 3					
	Order 4					

/3

15

13. Seven letters arrive at the Jones' house. The Jones' first names are Amy and Allen. All the letters are addressed to A. Jones.
Five of them are for Amy, the rest for Allen – but they don't know this.

a) What is the probability that the first letter opened will be for Amy? _____

b) What is the probability that the first letter opened will be for Allen? _____

/2

14. Write $\frac{147}{343}$ in its simplest terms. _____

/1

15. These are the average monthly temperatures in Alaska, near the North Pole.

Month	Jan	Feb	Mar	Apr	May	Jun	Jul	Aug	Sep	Oct	Nov	Dec
Temperature (°C)	−24	−10	−11	−1	9	15	16	13	6	−5	−17	−22

a) Which is the coldest month? _____

b) What is the difference in temperature between the warmest and coldest months?

_____ °C

c) For how many months is the temperature colder than −9 °C? _____

d) By how much does the temperature drop between November and December?

_____ °C

/4

16. This is a multiplication magic square. Numbers in rows, columns and diagonals **multiplied** together give the same answer. Find the missing numbers.

1.2	0.1	_____
0.9	_____	0.4
0.2	_____	0.3

/3

/40

PAPER 4

1. Find the smallest number that 2, 3, 4, 5 and 6 will divide into exactly. _____ /1

2. Use the fact that $6.2 \times 0.12 = 0.744$ to work out the answers to these calculations.

  a) $0.62 \times 1.2 =$ _____

b) $74.4 \div 6.2 =$ _____

c) $6.2 \times 0.012 =$ _____ /3

3. Janet keeps a record of how late her bus is in the morning. Here are her figures in minutes. A time of 0 minutes means that the bus arrives on time.

11	19	19	0	2	19	13	7	10	15
7	4	8	16	0	13	5	4	5	0
12	19	20	0	11	11	6	7	18	0

Use Janet's results to find the probability that the next morning her bus is:

a) on time _____

b) more than 5 minutes late. _____ /2

4. A shop sells two sizes of tape. Large tape costs £2.82 for 18.8 m. Small tape costs £1.92 for 12 m. Which tape gives better value for money?
Show the two calculations you need to do in order to work out the answer.

_____

_____ /2

5. This formula gives the area, A cm², of this L-shape involving x. (All lengths are in centimetres.)

$A = 40 - 2x$

a) What is the area of the L-shape when $x = 5$?

_____ cm²

b) Amy experiments with the formula. She finds that when $x = 0$, $A = 40$.
What has the formula calculated?

_____ /2

6. **a)** Translate this square 3 units to the right and 3 units down.

   b) Draw any lines of symmetry your final drawing has.

   c) What order of rotational symmetry does your final drawing have?

   _____

   d) Mark the centre of rotation with a cross.

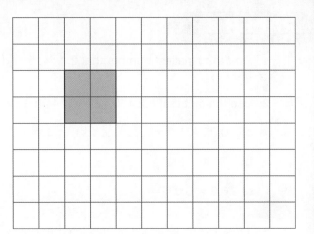

/4

7. It is estimated that approximately 9% of people are left-handed. The population of the UK is about 60 million.

   How many people in the UK are left-handed? _____ million

/1

8. Put a tick beside any of these statements that are true and a cross beside any that are false.

   0.875 > 0.90 _____   0.4 > 0.16 _____   0.15 > 0.125 + 0.03 _____

   0.01 + 0.99 = 0.100 _____   0.972 − 0.454 > 0.5 _____   0.3 × 0.3 = 0.9 _____

/3

9. The mean of four whole numbers is 5.

   a) What is the sum of the five numbers? _____

   b) Two of the numbers are 10 and 6. What could the other two numbers be?

   _____ and _____   _____ and _____   _____ and _____

/3

10. Use brackets to make each of these statements true.

   a) $(4 \times 5) + 5 = 25$ **b)** $(8 + 2 \times 2) + 5 = 25$

/2

11. Find the values of the lettered angles.

   $a = \underline{60^0}$ °

   $b = \underline{70^\circ}$ °

   $c = \underline{\hspace{2cm}}$ °

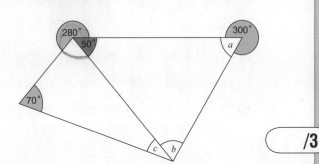

/3

12. This table shows the nutritional value of 100 g of banana (without the peel).

Calories	Carbohydrate (g)	Fat (g)	Fibre (g)	Sodium (g)
89	23	1	3	0.001

According to the International Banana Association an average-sized banana weighs 120 grams (without the peel).

a) How much fat is there in an average banana? _____ g

b) What percentage of a banana is fibre? _____ %

c) The maximum recommended daily intake of sodium is 2.4 g.
How many kilograms of bananas (without peel) would you need to reach this figure?

_____ kg

/3

13. This bar chart shows the average monthly temperatures in London (Canada), and London (UK).

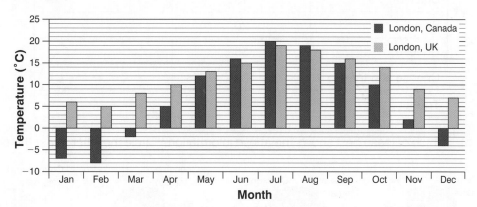

a) For which months was London, Canada, warmer than London, UK?

_____

b) What was the difference in temperature between the two Londons in March? _____ °C

c) For how many months is London, Canada, below −5 °C? _____

d) For which month(s) was the temperature difference greatest?

_____

/4

14. The students at a school voted on where to go on a school trip.
The choice was a theme park or London.
They voted 3 to 1 in favour of going to London.
Sixty students voted for London.
How many voted for going to the theme park? _____

/1

15. Here is a number sequence:

 0   2   4   6   8   ...

Write down the 66th number (term) in the sequence. _____

/1

16. In a survey, 120 students were asked to name their favourite sandwich.
The results are to be shown on a pie chart.

a) Complete the table below to show the pie chart angles for each sandwich.

Sandwich	Number of students	Pie chart angle
Chicken	13	
Salad	20	
Cheese	55	
Cheese and tomato	32	
Total:		

b) Which of these best shows the above information? Circle the letter under the pie chart.

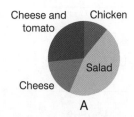
A

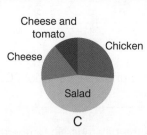
B   C

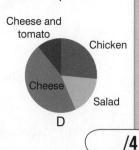
D

/4

17. Find as many 3-digit numbers as you can, which use the digits 1, 2 and 3
 once each and which are multiples of 4. _____

/1

/40

PAPER 5

1. For the numbers 60 and 10, the first number (60) is six times the second ($6 \times 10 = 60$).

 Which number must be added to both 60 and 10 so that the first number is double the second number? _____

/1

2. The mean of two numbers is 10. One of the numbers is 12.

What is the other number? _____

/1

3. Amy has made up a dice game. Three 1 to 6 dice are thrown. A person's score is the difference between the highest and lowest numbers showing.

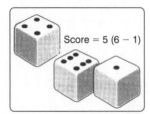

Score = 5 (6 − 1)

a) Amy keeps a record of the scores.

5	4	1	1	3	2	2	1	3	1	2	2
4	3	5	1	2	2	2	2	3	4	5	4
4	2	3	1	3	5	2	1	2	5	3	4
0	1	5	3	3	1	2	1	1	2	4	4
4	5	2	0	1	2	1	3	4	2	4	2

Complete this frequency table of scores.

Score	Tally	Frequency
0		
1		
2		
3		
4		
5		

b) What is the most likely score? _____

c) Estimate the probability of getting a score of 3. _____

/4

4. Amber can swim at a steady rate of 1.4 m each second.
Ben can swim at a steady rate of 0.8 m each second.

a) If they both start swimming together, how far ahead is Amber after 6.5 seconds?

_____

b) Amber can only keep swimming for two minutes, but Ben can keep swimming for three minutes. They are both able to keep up their steady speeds whilst swimming.

Who swam the furthest and by how much? _____ by _____ m   **/2**

5. What is the smallest perimeter a shape of area 11 cm² can have? Draw it on the

grid below. _____ cm

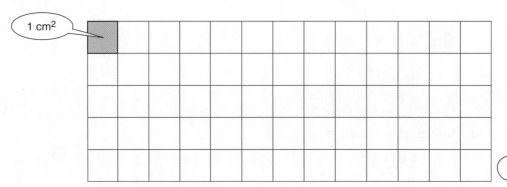

1 cm²

/1

6. This chart shows the average temperature in London, each day in August.

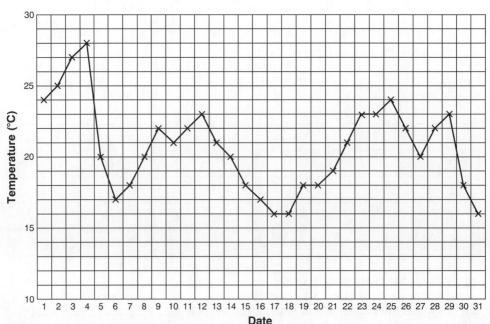

Temperature (°C)

Date

a) Calculate the mean temperature for the first and last weeks in August.

First week: _____ °C   Last week: _____ °C

On average which is the warmer week? _____

b) In what other way, apart from their means, did the temperatures in the first and

last week differ? _____

 /4

7. Fill in the missing numbers.

 a) $(45 \div \underline{\quad}) - 5 = 4$

b) $18 \div (\underline{\quad} - 4) = 6$

/2

8. Which one of these is the odd one out? Circle the correct answer.

$70 \div 100$ $14 \div 200$ 70% $\dfrac{14}{20}$ 0.7

$28 \div 40$ 0.70 $\dfrac{21}{30}$

/1

9. Complete this division grid.

÷	100	0.1	0.5
200	2	_____	400
40	0.4	400	_____
0.3	_____	3	0.6

/3

10. Anil works in a coffee shop. For standard coffee he mixes 3 scoops of coffee with 4 cups of water.
Which of these mixtures will make stronger coffee?

A   2 scoops with 3 cups of water   B   5 scoops with 8 cups of water
C   6 scoops with 9 cups of water   D   4 scoops with 5 cups of water

_____

 /1

11. These two rectangles have their matching sides parallel.

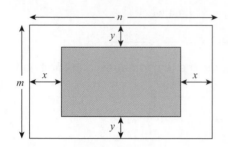

a) Write an expression for the perimeter of the grey rectangle.

_____

b) What perimeter does your expression give when $x = y = 0$?

_____

/2

12. This shape has rotational symmetry of order 3. Calculate angles a and b.

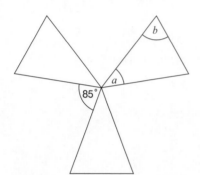

$a =$ _____ °

$b =$ _____ °

/2

13. 18-carat gold is 75% pure gold.

How much pure gold is there in a 60 g 18-carat ring? _____ g

/1

14. Solve these equations.

a) $3x = 12$ $x =$ _____

b) $x + x = 8$ $x =$ _____

/2

15. For safety, the foot of a ladder should stand away from the wall by a distance equal to a quarter of the height of the ladder.

A 10 m long ladder is put against a high wall. On a separate sheet of paper, use a scale of 1 cm representing 1 m to draw a scale drawing to find the angle the ladder makes with the horizontal.

_____ °

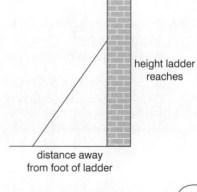

height ladder reaches

distance away from foot of ladder

/1

16. Complete these two diagrams so that each shape has rotational symmetry of order 2 with X as the centre of rotation.

a)

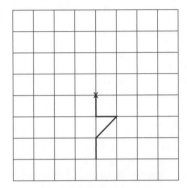

b)

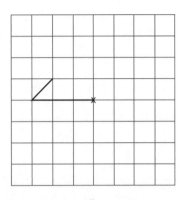

/2

17. a) Three of the corners (vertices) of a parallelogram are at (−2, −1), (0, 1) and (1, 0). Plot these points on the graph.

b) Find the coordinates of the three possible places for the fourth vertex.

(_____, _____)

(_____, _____)

(_____, _____)

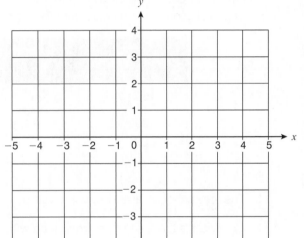

18. Approximate the answers to these calculations.

/4

 a) 87.9 × 2.97 is roughly _____ × _____ = _____

b) 490 ÷ 5.01 is roughly _____ ÷ _____ = _____

/2

19. A bag contains blue and red balls. The ratio of the blue balls to the red balls is 2 : 5

a) What is the minimum total number of balls in the bag? _____

/2

b) If there are 20 red balls in the bag, how many blue balls are there? _____

/2

20. Here are five digit cards.
Using just 1 or more of the five digit cards once only:

/2

a) what is the smallest number you can make that is more than thirty thousand? _____

/40

b) Make the largest number which is a multiple of 5. _____

PAPER 6

1. Here are some letters in Braille. Underneath each letter, write the number of lines of reflection and order of rotational symmetry each letter has.

Reflection _____   _____   _____   _____   _____

Rotation _____   _____   _____   _____   _____

/3

2. Two-stroke engines, like those used in petrol-driven grass mowers or mopeds, use a mixture of petrol and oil. The ratio, by volume of petrol to oil, can be from 16 : 1 to 100 : 1 depending on the engine. Complete this table for different mixtures.

Petrol : oil ratio	millilitres of oil per litre of petrol (to the nearest whole number)
50 : 1	
60 : 1	
70 : 1	

/3

3. The area, A, of an arrowhead is given by $A = \frac{1}{2}ab$.

   a) What is the area of an arrowhead with values of a and b of 4 m and 10 m?

   _____

   b) An arrowhead has an area of 80 cm². Its width, b, is 40 cm.

   What is its height, a? _____ cm

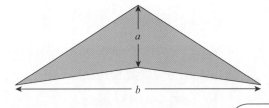

/3

4. By adding brackets, find the greatest value this expression can take.

   $$9 \times 6 + 4 \times 8 - 4$$ _____

/1

5. Find the missing digits.

   a) ___.03 + 2.1___ = 7.13   b) 8.___ − ___.5 = 5.9

/2

6. This is the design for a charity scratch card. It has 12 boxes. A player can scratch off just one box.

a) What is the probability of scratching a winning box?

_____

b) What is the probability of not scratching a winning box?

_____

c) How many of the boxes on this scratch card need to be winning boxes so that the probability of scratching a winning box is 20%?

_____

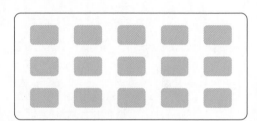

/3

7. This pie chart shows the results of an Internet survey into how many glasses of water people drank in a day.

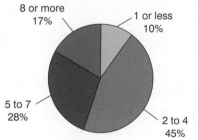

Number of glasses of water drunk a day

8 or more 17%
1 or less 10%
5 to 7 28%
2 to 4 45%

a) 113 people said they drank one glass or less. How many people took part in the survey?

_____

b) According to some doctors the average person should drink about 2 litres a day. By making an assumption about the capacity of an average glass, estimate how many glasses of water a day this is.

Assuming a glass is _____, 2 litres is about _____ glasses.

/3

8. Using two of these digit cards at a time, make three fractions that are:

a) less than $\frac{1}{2}$ _____   _____   _____

b) equal to $\frac{1}{2}$ _____   _____   _____

c) more than $\frac{1}{2}$ but less than 1 _____   _____   _____

/3

9. Solve these equations.

 a) $n + 2 = 7$ $n =$ _____

 b) $2 + x = 8$ $x =$ _____

 c) $3t = 12$ $t =$ _____

/3

10. This is a 9-piece tangram drawn on a centimetre square grid.

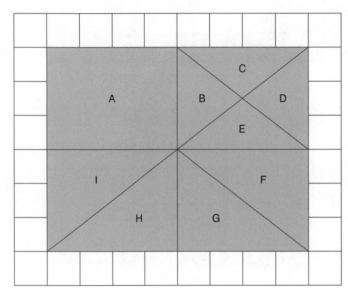

a) Calculate the area of piece A.

_____ cm²

b) Which piece has the largest perimeter?

_____

c) Which seven pieces make up three quarters of the whole tangram?

_____

d) Which of the pieces are isosceles triangles?

_____

/4

11. Make five calculations and their answers using these cards.

| 0.01 | 0.1 | 1 | 10 | 100 | × | ÷ | = |

For example: 10   ×   0.1   =   1

a) _____   **b)** _____

c) _____   **d)** _____

e) _____

/3

12. Neta wants to check her electricity bill for the period October to January. She knows the following facts:

- One unit of electricity = 1 kilowatt hour (kWh)
- The first 242 kWh used in this period are charged at £2.058p per kWh
- Any further kWh used are charged at £6.25p per kWh.

Calculate the amount she has to pay if the meter reading at the beginning of October was 79994 units and at the end of January was 81805 units. £ _____ /1

13. Helen buys a flute. It is on sale for cash at £400. She decides to buy it on "easy" terms. First she pays a deposit of 30%. Then she makes 12 monthly payments of £30. How much extra does she pay for the flute by buying it on "easy" terms?

£ _____ /1

14. At noon the temperature was 7 °C. By midnight it was −6 °C.

What was the drop in temperature? _____ °C /1

15. a) Estimate the height of this balloon above the ground.

The tree is about 10 m tall. _____ m

b) Measure the angle the rope makes with the horizontal.

_____ °

height above ground

c) The temperature drops as you go up into the air. This formula gives the drop in temperature, D °C, going up a height, h, metres:

$$D = \frac{h}{200}$$

What is the drop in temperature when a balloon goes up 400 m?

_____ °C /3

16. Find the values of the angles marked a, b and c.

$a =$ _____ °

$b =$ _____ °

$c =$ _____ °

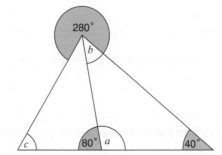

/3

/40

PAPER 7

1. This double bar chart compares the lengths of words (number of letters) in English and Swedish.

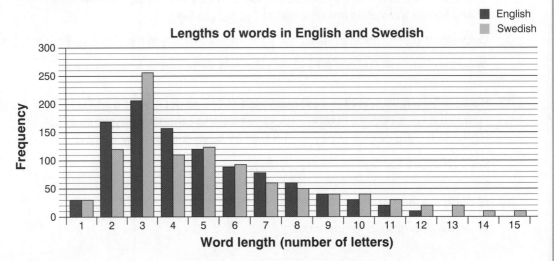

Put a tick beside true statements and a cross beside false ones.

a) Swedish has more long words than English. _____

b) The modal word length is the same in both languages. _____

c) About 20% of Swedish words are 3 letters long. _____

d) About 30% of English words are one letter long. _____

e) The mean average word length in both languages is about 4 to 5 letters. _____

f) About 40 words in both languages were 9 letters long. _____

g) There are more two letter words in English than Swedish. _____

/4

2. In a diving competition Liz scored 60.1, 65.7 and 69.2 points for her first three dives. Anita scored 56.1, 73.3 and 62.9 points for her first 3 dives. Each competitor's scores are added together to give their total for the competition.

a) After 3 dives who was winning and by how much?

_____ by _____ points

b) Anita won the competition. For her 4th and final dive Liz scored 71.1 points. What was the minimum number of points Anita must have scored in order to win?

_____ points

/2

3. Put a cross beside any of these calculations that are obviously wrong.

 a) $23 \times 127 = 2921$ _____

b) $45 \times 191 = 8596$ _____

c) $1025 \div 5 = 25$ _____

d) $9.9 + 6.3 + 1.99 = 28.19$ _____

e) $129.01 - 19.4 = 109.61$ _____

f) $15.9 - 7.9 = 8$ _____

/2

4. A car needs 10 litres of petrol to travel 120 km. How many litres are needed to travel

 360 km? _____ litres

/1

5. Fill in the missing numbers, using only the numbers in the box.

0.04	0.4	2	0.1

a) _____ × _____ = 0.08

b) _____ ÷ _____ = 20

c) _____ ÷ _____ = 0.1

d) _____ × _____ = 0.8

/4

6. These three square patterns are made out of black and white squares.

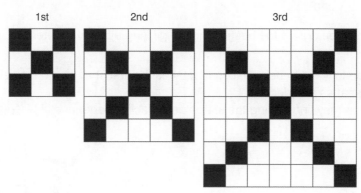

1st   2nd   3rd

The pattern continues ...

a) What is the total number of squares in each of the next two patterns?

_____   _____

b) Count the number of black squares in each pattern. Write the next four terms in the sequence.

_____   _____   _____   _____

c) Write down the first five terms in the sequence made from the number of white squares.

/3

_____   _____   _____   _____   _____

7. Bronze is an alloy made from mixtures of tin and copper.

a) A type of bronze called gun metal, used for statues, is 90% copper and 10% tin by weight.

(i) What is the ratio of copper to tin in gun metal? _____

(ii) What weight of tin is there in a gun metal statue weighing 500 kg? _____ g

b) Bell bronze is used to make bells. It is made from copper and tin in the ratio 39 : 11.

What percentage of bell bronze is copper? _____ %

/3

8. Three bags contain black, grey and white counters. A counter is taken without looking from each bag.

a) What is the probability that the counter from C is grey?

_____

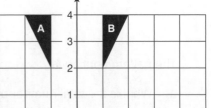

b) For two of the bags the probability of taking a grey counter is the same. Which are they?

_____ and _____

c) Which bag gives the best chance of picking a black counter? _____

/3

9. Describe fully the transformation that takes the first shape onto the second shape. All the shapes are identical.
(N.B. You may find tracing the shape onto tracing paper useful.)

a) A to B

_____

b) B to D

_____

c) A to C

_____

d) B to C

_____

e) C to A

_____

/5

10. The line of dots continues in each direction.

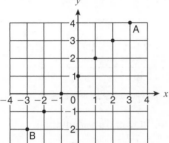

a) What are the coordinates of dot B? (_____, _____)

b) What are the coordinates of the unseen dot before B?

(_____, _____)

c) Circle any of these points that will have dots on them.

(6, 5)   (10, 11)   (−10, −11)

(−11, −10)   (100, 101)

/4

/1

11. Grapes cost £2.40p for 800 grams. What will the cost of 250 grams be? £ _____

12. I think of a number, double it and square the result. The answer is 100.

What number did I first think of? _____

/1

13. ABCDE is a regular pentagon.

a) What name is given to triangles like

ABE and BDE? _____

b) Calculate the values of x and y.

$x =$ _____° $y =$ _____°

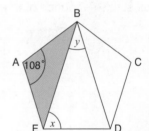

/3

14. a) Estimate the total length of this Boeing 747.

The airport coach is 10 m long. _____ m

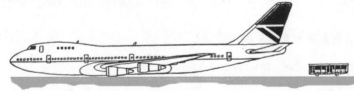

b) A Boeing 747 can hold 452 passengers.
How many Boeing 747s would be needed to evacuate 1600 refugees from a war zone?

_____

c) The planes used by a budget transatlantic firm have three classes: 1st class, premium economy and economy. In total there are 348 seats, of these 75% are economy, 29 are 1st class and the rest are premium economy.

/4

(i) How many seats are economy class? _____

(ii) What fraction of the total number of seats are premium

economy class? _____

/40

PAPER 8

1. This is the temperature outside one night.

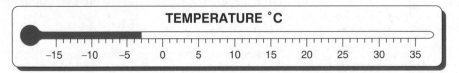

TEMPERATURE °C

−15 −10 −5 0 5 10 15 20 25 30 35

    a)   The temperature inside is 21 °C. How much warmer is this than outside?

       _____ °C

    b)   The next night the temperature rose by 3 °C.

       What was the temperature that night?_____ °C

/2

2. Look at this sequence of three shapes drawn on centimetre square paper.

Pattern 1   Pattern 2   Pattern 3

The pattern continues in the same way.

    a)   Complete this table about the shapes.

Pattern	1	2	3	4
Area (cm²)	1	3	5	_____
Perimeter (cm)	4	8	_____	_____

    b)   What is the perimeter of the 100th L-shape in the pattern? _____ cm

    c)   What is the perimeter of the nth L-shape in the pattern? _____ cm

    d)   For each pattern number look at the difference between the numbers giving the area
       and perimeter. What is the name given to this sequence of numbers?

/6

_____

3. This is a list of the first 20 prime numbers:

2	3	5	7	11	13	17	19	23	29
31	37	(41)	43	47	53	59	61	67	(71)

a) Find two different prime numbers whose product is 2911.

_____ and _____

b) How can you tell just by looking that 7612956 cannot be the product of two primes?

_____ /2

4. Complete the table describing fully the symmetry of each of these logos.

A   B   C   D

Logo	Order of rotational symmetry	Number of lines of symmetry	Logo	Order of rotational symmetry	Number of lines of symmetry
A			C		
B			D		

/3

5.

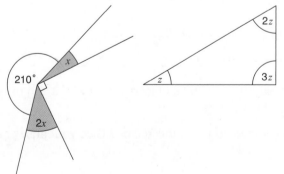

a) Find the value of x.

$x =$ _____

b) Find the value of z.

$z =$ ___30°___

/2

6. A sample of people were asked what their favourite pet was.
A total of 390 people voted for dogs. All the results are displayed in this pie chart.

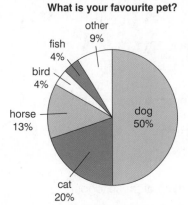

What is your favourite pet?

a) How many people took part in the survey?

_____

b) How many of the people surveyed voted for cats?

_____

c) What fraction of the people voted for cats?

_____

/3

7. Write the correct units for these estimated measurements.

a) The width of a little finger is 1 _____

b) The diameter of a full stop is 1 _____

c) The length of a petrol tanker is 1000 _____

d) The width of a pencil line is 0.001 _____

e) The length of a pencil is 0.15 _____

f) The thickness of a plastic card is 0.2 _____

/3

8. Janine works in a cafe making smoothies.
She can make one "Strawberry Special" out of 6 fresh strawberries and 4 scoops
of ice-cream. She has 48 strawberries.

a) How many "Strawberry Specials" could she make? _____

b) How many scoops of ice-cream will she need? _____

c) Janine finds another recipe that says to mix 250 g of iced yogurt with 375 g of
strawberries, which will make four smoothies.

What is the ratio of strawberries to iced yogurt in this recipe? Give your answer as
the simplest ratio.

_____ : _____

/3

9. Derek keys a number into his calculator. He multiplies the number by 6.17 and adds 0.046. The answer shown on the calculator is 100.

What number did he key in first? _____   /1

10. Besco stocks 500 ml bottles of diet cola for 85p. Baza only stocks the 1.25 litre bottle. The manager wants to sell it at a price that is just as good value as Besco.

What is the most she can charge for one of her 1.25 litre bottles? _____   /2

11. A rectangle has a perimeter of 26 m and an area of 36 m².

What are two dimensions of the rectangle? _____ m by _____ m   /1

12. A large oil tanker is being unloaded. The depth of oil in the tanker, d metres, is given by $d = 20 - 2t$, where t hours is the time the pumps have been pumping.

a) What is the depth of oil in the tanker after 2 hours of pumping? _____ m

b) How many hours will it take to empty the tanker? _____ hours   /2

13. Write these lengths in order, putting the shortest first.

387 cm   3.9 m   4.07 m   450 cm   3.49 m   3.785 m   6.6 m

_____   /1

14. Kwan wants to estimate how many pages his English project will take up.
First he counts how many words he types on a line.
Here are his results for 30 lines picked at random from an old English project he did.

15	18	17	19	18	15	16	15	18	19
17	18	15	18	17	18	18	15	15	19
18	19	17	17	17	18	18	15	16	15

a) Calculate the average number of words on a line.
State whether you used the mean, median or mode.

The _____ average is _____

b) With his word processor settings Kwan is able to get 24 lines on a page.
His project, which has no pictures and is all text, should be about 5000 words long.

How many sides of paper will Kwan's project be? _____ sides   /3

15. Look at these thought bubbles. What shape or shapes might Amber have been thinking about?

It has four sides...

...but none of them are parallel.

Pairs of sides have the same length.

/1

16. Find the missing numbers to make the answers to these calculations correct.

a) $0.60 \div$ _____ $= 0.06$

b) $1 \div$ _____ $= 0.01$

/3

c) $6.1 \times$ _____ $= 610$

17.

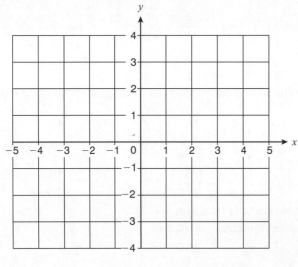

a) Mark and label the three points A $(-2, 2)$, B $(2, 1)$ and C $(-3, -1)$

b) Which of the three points is nearest to the origin?

_____

/2

/40

PAPER 9

1. Write the number of lines of symmetry the following shapes have:

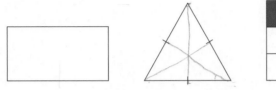 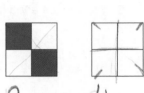

a) ___2___   b) ___3___   c) ___1___   d) ___2___   e) ___4___

/5

2. Convert the following metric units into imperial measures:

a) 23 m = ___2300___ cm

b) 150 m = ___0.150___ km

c) 25 km = ___25,000___ m

d) 5 cm = ___0.05___ m

/4

3. Simon buys the following packets of crisps from the supermarket:

- 2 Salt & Vinegar
- 3 Ready Salted
- 3 Prawn Cocktail
- 1 Barbecue Beef

He takes out one packet at random and eats it.

a) What is the probability he picks Ready Salted? _____

b) What is the probability he picks Salt & Vinegar or Barbecue Beef? _____

c) What is the probability he did not pick Prawn Cocktail? _____

d) What is the probability he picks Cheese & Onion? _____

/4

4. You are told that 148 × 23 = 3404.
   Without using a calculator, write down the answers to the following:

a) 148 × 2.3 = _____

b) 0.148 × 23 = _____

c) 14.8 × 2.3 = _____

d) 3404 ÷ 2.3 = _____

/4

5. Melissa and Dillon buy a large box of chocolates and share them in the ratio 2 : 3. If Melissa takes out 10 chocolates, how many were there in the box all together?

_____

/2

6. Solve these equations.

   a) $4x - 3 = 9$ $x =$ _____

   b) $4x + 3 = 9$ $x =$ _____

   c) $4x - 3 = -9$ $x =$ _____

/3

7. At Milena's Cupcake Emporium, you can buy cupcakes in a box of 4 costing £5.00, or in a gift-wrapped box of 9 costing £11.50.
   Which box offers the best value for money?

   The box of _____ cupcakes.

/1

8. Find the angle x in the following shapes:

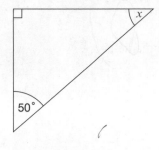 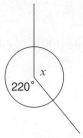 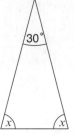 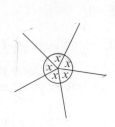

   a) ___40°___   **b)** ___140°___   **c)** ___75°___   **d)** ___72°___

/4

9. Asif travels from London to Lancaster on the train, a journey taking three hours.
   He spends:

   - $\frac{1}{5}$ of his time reading his magazines.

   - 65% of the time listening to his mp3 player.

   a) How long (in minutes) does he spend reading magazines?   _____

   b) How long (in minutes) does he spend listening to his mp3 player? _____

/2

10. At Emily's fruit stall, a banana costs x pence and a lemon costs y pence.
    Find the answers to the following, using x and y.

    a) How much will two lemons cost? _____ pence

    b) How much will one banana and one lemon cost? _____ pence

c) How much change will I get from a £1 coin after buying five bananas?

_____ pence

11. Work out the following calculations.

a) $4 - 6 =$ _____

b) $-4 - 3 =$ _____

c) $10 - (-3) =$ _____

12. Look at the following three diagrams:

Diagram 1   Diagram 2   Diagram 3

When n represents the diagram number:

- The formula for the number of black circles in each diagram is given by $2n$
- The formula for the number of white circles in each diagram is given by $n - 1$

a) How many **total** circles will there be in the 10th diagram? _____

b) Which diagram will have 41 circles in total? _____

13. A rectangle is formed by plotting four coordinates on a cm^2 grid and joining them in turn by straight lines.

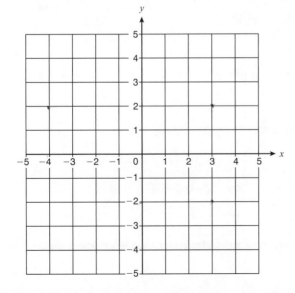

Three of the coordinates are $(3, -2)$, $(3, 2)$ and $(-4, 2)$.

a) State the missing coordinate.

(_____, _____)

b) Plot the coordinates on the axes given, and shade the rectangle.

c) Find the area of the rectangle you have drawn.

_____ cm^2

PAPER 10

1. A bottle of vinegar normally contains 400 ml. A special offer gives an extra 30%.

   How much vinegar is there in the special offer bottle? _____ ml   `/1`

2. A fair eight-sided dice numbered 1 to 8 is thrown.
   The number showing is squared and the last digit of the answer is a person's score.

   a) (i) List all the possible scores. _____

   (ii) How many different scores are possible? _____

   b) What is the probability of **not** scoring 1? _____   `/4`

3. I think of a number. I multiply it by 7. I subtract 32. The result is 3 times the number I started with. Let the number I first thought of be x.

   a) Use the information above to write an equation involving x.

   _____

   b) Solve your equation to find the value of x. _____   `/2`

4. On an archery target the diameter of the inner and outer bull's eye is 6 cm and 12 cm.
   Taking π to be 3.1 calculate:

   a) the area of the inner bull's eye _____ cm²

   b) the area of the outer bull's eye. _____ cm²   `/2`

   6 cm
   ←12 cm→

5. The internal angles of a quadrilateral are $x°$, $2x°$, $3x°$ and $4x°$.
   What are the values, in degrees, of the four angles?

   _____ °   _____ °   _____ °   _____ °   `/1`

6. Find, to the nearest whole number, the value of x which gives $x(x^2 - 3)$ a value of 1000.

   _____   `/2`

7. Put a cross next to the sums where the answers are obviously wrong.

   a) 19% of 42 kg = 7.98 kg _____   **b)** 35% of £18 = £11.50 _____

   c) 49% of 9.43 m = 5.01 m _____   **d)** 9% of 21.70 g = 2.19 g _____

   e) 76% of £4.25 = £3.23 _____   **f)** 35% of 33.5 cm = 10.98 m _____

   g) 21% of 83 g = 17.43 g _____   **h)** 57% of £12.50 = £6.20 _____   `/3`

8.

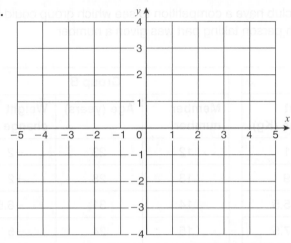

a) Draw an L-shape whose corners are given by $(-2, 1)$, $(-2, 0)$ and $(-1.5, 0)$.

b) Draw an enlargement of your L-shape with scale factor 2 and centre of enlargement $(-5, -2)$.

Leave in any construction lines that you draw.

/3

9. Here are two types of commands for moving a model turtle.

> FD 10 means move forward 10 cm
>
> RT 30 means turn 30° clockwise

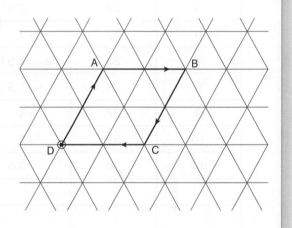

Starting from D, write the commands to draw a parallelogram on this 1 cm triangle paper.
The path from D to A has already been written

RT 30   FD 2 _____

_____

/3

10. Solve these equations.

a) $2x = 10$ $x =$ _____

b) $2(x + 1) = 20$ $x =$ _____

c) $3x = x + 18$ $x =$ _____

/3

11. Which of these equations pass through the point $(1, 1)$ when plotted as straight lines?

A $y = 2x$ **B** $y = x + 1$ **C** $y = x$ **D** $y = 2x - 1$ **E** $y = 5x - 4$

_____

/1

12. Two groups of people in a health club have a competition to see which group could lose the most weight in 6 months. Each person taking part was given a number.
This table shows the results:

Group A			Group B		
Member number	Age (years)	Weight change (Kg)	Member number	Age (years)	Weight change (Kg)
1	31	−1	12	23	−2
2	25	−9	13	28	+2
3	29	−5.5	14	31	−6.5
4	24	−7.5	15	24	−5
5	30	−2.5	16	25	−6.5
6	32	+3	17	30	+0.5
7	23	−1.5	18	24	−9
8	28	−11.5	19	30	−5
9	27	+4	20	31	−3.5
10	31	+2	21	27	+2.5
11	26	−0.5	22	27	−5.5
			23	29	−1.5
			24	29	+2.5

a) Which person lost the most weight? _____

b) Which person gained the most weight? _____

c) Which group lost the most weight? _____

d) What was the overall average weight loss for each group? _____

/4

13. Write these fractions in order of size, smallest first.

$$\frac{3}{5} \qquad \frac{17}{20} \qquad \frac{7}{10} \qquad \frac{5}{8} \qquad \frac{3}{4}$$

_____

/1

Answer booklet: KS3 Maths Levels 5–6

Paper 1

1. $\left(\frac{2}{3}, \frac{8}{12}\right)$ and $\left(\frac{6}{8}, \frac{21}{28}, \frac{30}{40}\right)$ and $\left(\frac{25}{35}, \frac{10}{14}\right)$ *(2 marks: 1 if one correct group)*
2. a) 1 ml
   b) 333 or 333.3 .... hours or 14 *(2 marks each: 1 for*
   or 13.8 ... days *'number,' 1 for 'unit')*
3. a) (i) House wall   (ii) Garden wall
   b) 5 *(1 mark each)*
4. Mean = 8   Range = 10 *(1 mark each)*
5. Tom by 630 m *(1 mark)*
6. In range (26 to 28)° *(1 mark)*
7. a) Newcastle   b) Glasgow
   c) Bristol *(1 mark each)*
8. a) 403   b) 11009 *(1 mark each)*
9. 7%, 10%, $\frac{15}{100}$, a quarter, 0.3, 0.7 *(1 mark)*
10. a) 100   b) 0.01 *(1 mark each)*
11. Trafalgar Square by 850 m² *(1 mark for correct square,*
   1 for number)
12. 40°   40° *(1 mark)*
13. a) ✗   b) R
    c) ✓   d) ✗ *(2 marks: 1 mark if one error)*
14. a) 24   b) 3 *(1 mark each)*
15. a)

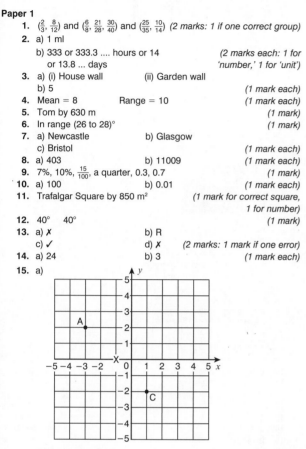

   b) B(1, 2) D(−3, −2) *(1 mark each)*
16. 790.5 *(1 mark)*
17. In range (3 to 7)° *(1 mark)*
18. a) $r = \frac{w}{t}$ b) 212 *(1 mark each)*
19. a) $\frac{3}{10}$ b) $\frac{5}{10}$ or $\frac{1}{2}$
    c) $\frac{1}{10}$ *(1 mark each)*
20. a) 5   b) 4 *(1 mark each)*

Paper 2

1. a) $\frac{2}{9}$ b) $\frac{3}{9}$ or $\frac{1}{3}$
   c) $\frac{7}{9}$ *(1 mark each)*
2. Lines of symmetry   0   0
   Order of rotation   2   4 *(1 mark for each correct pair)*
3. 1½ g, 2.00 g, 0.01 kg, 0.1 kg, ½ kg, 2.0 kg, 20 kg *(1 mark)*
4. a) $P = 4g + 3s + b$ *(1 mark)*
   b) $g = 2\ 1\ 1\ 0\ 0\ 0$
   $s = 0\ 1\ 0\ 2\ 1\ 0$
   $b = 0\ 1\ 4\ 2\ 5\ 8$ *(2 marks: 1 mark if 4 or 5 listed)*
5. a) $7 + 2 \times (9 + 6) = 37$
   b) $(7 + 2) \times 9 + 6 = 87$ *(1 mark each)*
6. 40° and 100° *(2 marks)*
   70° and 70° *(1 mark)*
7. a) January   b) 10
   c) 30° *(1 mark each)*
8. a) 4 : 3   (i)   (iii)
   b) 16 : 9 (ii)   (iv) *(1 mark each)*

9. b = in range (6.6 to 7) cm
   a = in range (39 to 43)° *(1 mark each)*
10. a) 8   b) 45 *(1 mark each)*
11. $\frac{8}{32}$ or $\frac{2}{8}$ *(1 mark each)*
12. a) Points A, B and C plotted. *(2 marks: 1 if one error)*

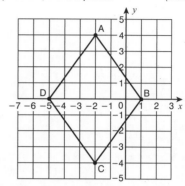

    b) D (−5 , 0) *(1 mark)*
    c) 24 (or 22 to 26 if by counting) *(1 mark)*
13. a) T = 45*l* + 25*s* + 20*c*
    b) T/100 or (45*l* + 25*s* + 20*c*)/100 *(1 mark each)*
14. a) 11   b) 4 *(1 mark each)*
15. a) 60% circled   b) 10 : 6 or 5 : 3
    c) two more tiles need shading *(1 mark each)*
16. a) 680   b) January
    c) two possible answers: Feb and Oct, or Apr and Aug
    d) 55 *(1 mark each)*

Paper 3

1. a) (i) P = 10*a*   (ii) P = 14*a*
   b) 4*a* *(1 mark each)*
2. a) 12   b) 28 *(1 mark each)*
3. a) 9 and 29
   b) 2 possible answers: 35 and 41 or 29 and 35
   c) 41 and 59 *(1 mark each)*
4. Area = 10000 cm²   Perimeter = 400 cm *(1 mark each)*
5. a) 45   b) 198
   c) 199.15 *(1 mark each)*
6. a) (−2, −1)   (−4, 3) *(1 mark each)*
   b) (3, 1) *(1 mark)*
7. a) 5   b) 2
   c) 0.13   d) 5 *(1 mark each)*
8. a) 3   b) 1101 *(1 mark each)*
9. Any decimal between, but not including, 0.75 and 0.9. *(1 mark)*
10. 35°, 75° and 70° (A, B and E) *(1 mark)*
11. a) (i) In the range (3.5 to 4.5) m
    (ii) In range (9 to 11) m
    b) In range (£40 to £38) *(1 mark each)*
12.

		Number of lines of reflection symmetry					
		None	1	2	3	3	
Rotation symmetry	None	A, E	B, D				
	Order 2			C			
	Order 3						
	Order 4						

(3 marks: 1 for each correctly filled in box)

1

13. a) $\frac{5}{7}$ b) $\frac{2}{7}$ *(1 mark each)*

14. $\frac{3}{7}$ *(1 mark)*

15. a) Jan
    b) 40°C
    c) 5
    d) 5°C   *(1 mark each)*

16. *(3 marks: 1 for each correct cell)*

1.2	0.1	**1.8**
0.9	**0.6**	0.4
0.2	**3.6**	0.3

Paper 4

1. 60   *(1 mark)*
2. a) 0.744   b) 12
   c) 0.0744   *(1 mark each)*
3. a) $\frac{5}{30}$ or $\frac{1}{6}$
   b) $\frac{20}{30}$ or $\frac{2}{3}$ *(1 mark each)*
4. $2.82 \div 18.8$ or $18.8 \div 2.82$ and
   $1.92 \div 12$ or $12 \div 1.92$

   So 18.8 m roll of tape is the better value.   *(1 mark for showing working out, 1 for answer)*
5. a) 30
   b) The area of a rectangle 10 cm by 4 cm   *(1 mark each)*
6. a) Grey square drawn.   *(1 mark)*

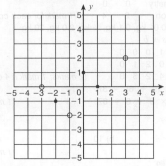

   b) 2 lines of symmetry drawn   *(1 mark)*
   c) Order-2   d) marked with a cross   *(1 mark each)*
7. 5.4 million   *(1 mark)*
8. ✗ ✓ ✗
   ✗ ✓ ✗   *(3 marks: −1 for each error)*
9. a) 20   *(1 mark)*
   b) 1 and 3   2 and 2   4 and 0   *(2 marks for two or more correct)*
10. a) $(4 \times 5) + 5 = 25$
    b) $(8 + 2) \times 2 + 5 = 25$ *(1 mark each)*
11. $a = 60°$
    $b = 70°$
    $c = 80°$ *(1 mark each)*
12. a) 12
    b) 3
    c) 240   *(1 mark each)*
13. a) June, July, August   b) 10
    c) 2
    d) January, February   *(1 mark each)*
14. 20   *(1 mark)*
15. 130   *(1 mark)*
16. a)   *(3 marks: 2 if three correct, 1 if two correct)*

Sandwich	Number of students	Pie chart angle
Chicken	13	39°
Salad	20	60°
Cheese	55	165°
Cheese and tomato	32	96°
Total:	120	360°

   b) B circled   *(1 mark)*
17. 132 and 312   *(1 mark)*

Paper 5
1. 40   *(1 mark)*
2. 8   *(1 mark)*
3. a)   *(2 marks: 1 if one error)*

Score	Frequency
0	2
1	13
2	17
3	10
4	11
5	7

   b) 2   c) $\frac{10}{60}$ or $\frac{1}{6}$ *(1 mark each)*
4. a) 3.9 m   b) Amber by 24 m   *(1 mark each)*
5. 14 (using whole squares)   *(1 mark)*

6. a) First week = 22.7 °C   Last week = 20.7 °C
   1st week is warmer   *(3 marks)*
   b) 1ˢᵗ week has wider range or
   two peaks in last week   *(1 mark)*
7. a) 5   b) 7   *(1 mark each)*
8. Odd one out is $14 \div 200$ *(1 mark)*
9.

÷	100	0.1	0.5
200	2	**2000**	400
40	0.4	400	**80**
0.3	**0.003**	3	0.6

     (3 marks)

10. Only D is stronger   *(1 mark)*
11. a) $2n - 4x + 2m - 4y$
    b) $2n + 2m$ or equivalent   *(1 mark each)*
12. a) 35°   b) 72.5°   *(1 mark each)*
13. 45   *(1 mark)*
14. a) 4   b) 4   *(1 mark each)*
15. In range (74 to 78)°   *(1 mark)*
16. a) e.g.   b) e.g.

     (1 mark each)

17. a) 3 vertices indicated   *(1 mark)*

   b) (3, 2)
   (−1, −2)
   (−3, 0)   *(3 marks)*

18. a) 87.9×2.97 is roughly $90 \times 3 = 270$
b) $490 \div 5.01$ is roughly $500 \div 5 = 100$ *(1 mark each)*
19. a) 7 b) 8 *(1 mark each)*
20. a) 31578 b) 87315 *(1 mark each)*

Paper 6

1. Ref. 1 2 0 0 0 *(3 marks: 2 if four correct,*
Rot. 0 2 0 2 0 *1 if three correct)*

2.

Petrol : oil ratio	millilitres of oil per litre of petrol (to the nearest whole number)
50 : 1	20
60 : 1	17
70 : 1	14

(3 marks)

3. a) 20 m² *(2 marks: 1 for number, 1 for units)*
b) 4 cm *(1 mark)*
4. $9 \times (6 + 4) \times 8 - 4 = 716$ *(1 mark)*
5. a) **5.**03 $+$ 2.**10** $= 7.13$
b) **8.**4 $-$ **2.**5 $= 5.9$ *(1 mark each)*
6. a) $\frac{2}{12}$ or $\frac{1}{6}$
b) $\frac{10}{12}$ or $\frac{5}{6}$
c) 3 *(1 mark each)*
7. a) 1130 *(1 mark)*
b) (200−300) ml
(10 to 7) glasses *(2 marks)*
8. a) $\frac{2}{6}$ $\frac{2}{8}$ $\frac{3}{8}$
b) $\frac{2}{4}$ $\frac{3}{6}$ $\frac{4}{8}$
c) $\frac{2}{3}$ $\frac{3}{4}$ $\frac{4}{6}$ or $\frac{6}{8}$ *(1 mark each)*
9. a) 5
b) 6
c) 4 *(1 mark each)*
10. a) 12
b) A
c) A B C D E I H or A B C D E F G
d) B D E C *(1 mark each)*
11. for example $10 \times 0.01 = 0.1$ $100 \times 0.1 = 10$
$100 \times 0.01 = 1$ $10 \div 0.1 = 100$ *(3 marks for any 5 correct,*
$1 \div 0.1 = 10$ $0.1 \div 0.01 = 10$ *2 for any four, 1 for any three)*
12. £103.04 *(1 mark)*
13. £80 *(1 mark)*
14. 13 °C *(1 mark)*
15. a) In range (25 to 35) m
b) In range (35–40) °C
c) 2 °C *(1 mark each)*
16. a) 100° b) 40°
c) 60° *(1 mark each)*

Paper 7

1. a) ✓ b) ✓ c) ✗ d) ✗
e) ✓ f) ✓ g) ✓ *(4 marks: −1 for each error)*
2. a) Liz by 2.7 points
b) 73.9 *(1 mark each)*
3. a) ____ b) ____
c) ✗ d) ✗ *(2 marks: −1*
e) ____ f) ____ *for each error)*
4. 30 *(1 mark)*
5. a) 0.04×2 b) $2 \div 0.1$
c) $0.04 \div 0.4$ d) 2×0.4 *(1 mark each)*
6. a) 81, 121 b) 5, 9, 13, 17, 21, 25, 29
c) 4, 16, 36, 64, 100 *(1 mark each)*
7. a) (i) 9 : 1 (ii) 50g
b) 78% *(1 mark each)*
8. a) $\frac{4}{10}$ or $\frac{2}{5}$ b) A and C
c) A *(1 mark each)*

9. a) reflection in y-axis
b) ½ turn rotation about the origin
c) ½ turn rotation about the origin
d) reflection in x-axis
e) ½ turn rotation about the origin *(1 mark each)*
10. a) $(-3, -2)$ *(1 mark)*
b) $(-4, -3)$ *(1 mark)*
c) (10, 11), $(-11, -10)$, (100, 101) *(2 marks: 1 for one correct)*
11. £0.75 or 75p *(1 mark)*
12. 5 *(1 mark)*
13. a) isosceles triangle *(1 mark)*
b) $x = 72°$
$y = 36°$ *(2 marks)*
14. a) In range (65 to 85) m b) 4
c) (i) 261 (ii) $\frac{1}{6}$ *(1 mark each)*

Paper 8

1. a) 24 °C b) 0 °C *(1 mark each)*
2. a)

Pattern	1	2	3	4
Area (cm²)	1	3	5	7
Perimeter (cm)	4	8	12	16

(3 marks: 1 for each correct)

b) 400 c) $4n$ *(1 mark each)*
d) Odd numbers *(1 mark)*
3. a) 41 and 71
b) Can only end with a 1, 3, 7 or 9 *(1 mark each)*
4.

Logo	Order of rotation symmetry	Number of lines of symmetry	Logo	Order of rotation symmetry	Number of lines of symmetry
A	0	1	C	3	3
B	2	2	D	2	0

(3 marks: 2 if one cell error, 1 if two cell errors)

5. a) 20° b) 30° *(1 mark each)*
6. a) 780 b) 156
c) $\frac{1}{5}$ *(1 mark each)*
7. a) cm b) mm
c) cm d) m *(3 marks: 2 if one*
e) m f) cm *error, 1 if two errors)*
8. a) 8 b) 32
c) 3:2 *(1 mark each)*
9. 16.2 *(1 mark)*
10. £2.12 (212p) or £2.11 (211p) *(2 marks: 1 for number,*
1 for units)
11. 4 m by 9 m *(1 mark)*
12. a) 16 m b) 10 hours *(1 mark each)*
13. 3.49 m, 3.785 m, 387 cm, 3.9 m, 4.07 m, 450 cm, 6.6 m *(1 mark)*
14. a) mean = 17 *(2 marks: 1 for*
mode = 18 *measure, 1 for*
median = 17 *number)*
b) 12 or 13 sides *(1 mark)*
15. Arrowhead, kite *(1 mark)*
16. a) 10 b) 100
c) 100 *(1 mark each)*
17. a)

b) B *(1 mark each)*

Paper 9

1. 2, 3, 1, 2, 4

   a) 2   b) 3   c) 1   d) 2   e) 4
                                                  (1 mark each)

2. a) 2300   b) 0.150
   c) 25000   d) 0.05   *(1 mark each)*

3. a) $\frac{3}{9}$ or $\frac{1}{3}$
   b) $\frac{3}{9}$ or $\frac{1}{3}$
   c) $\frac{6}{9}$ or $\frac{2}{3}$
   d) 0   *(1 mark each)*

4. a) 340.4   b) 3.404
   c) 34.04   d) 1480   *(1 mark each)*

5. 25   *(2 marks)*

6. a) $x = 3$
   b) $x = \frac{6}{4}$ or $\frac{3}{2}$ or $1\frac{1}{2}$
   c) $x = -\frac{6}{4}$ or $-\frac{3}{2}$ or $-1\frac{1}{2}$ *(1 mark each)*

7. 4   *(1 mark)*

8. a) $x = 40°$ b) $x = 140°$
   c) $x = 75°$ d) $x = 72°$ *(1 mark each)*

9. a) 36
   b) 117   *(1 mark each)*

10. a) $2y$
   b) $x + y$
   c) $100 - 5x$ *(1 mark each)*

11. a) -2
   b) -7
   c) 13   *(1 mark each)*

12. a) 29
   b) Diagram 14   *(1 mark each)*

13. a) $(-4, -2)$
   b)

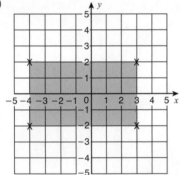

   c) 28 cm²   *(1 mark each)*

Paper 10

1. 520   *(1 mark)*

2. a) (i) 1 4 9 6 5 6 9 4   *(2 marks: 1 mark if one omission)*
      (ii) 5   *(1 mark)*
   b) $\frac{7}{8}$ *(1 mark)*

3. a) $7x - 32 = 3x$ or $4x = 32$
   b) 8   *(1 mark each)*

4. a) 27.9
   b) 83.7   *(1 mark each)*

5. 36°   72°   108°   144°   *(1 mark)*

6. 10   *(2 marks)*

7. a) _____   b) ✗   c) ✗   *(3 marks: 2 if*
   d) ✗   e) _____   f) ✗   *one error, 1 if*
   g) _____   h) ✗   *two errors)*

---

8. a) Grey L-shape   *(1 mark)*

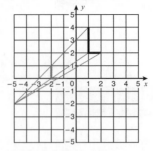

   b) Enlarged shape
      Centre of enlargement at $(-5, -2)$ *(2 marks)*

9. RT 30   FD 2   RT 60   FD 2
   RT 120   FD 2   RT 60   FD 2   *(3 marks)*

10. a) 5   b) 9
   c) 9   *(1 mark each)*

11. **C** $y = x$, **D** $y = 2x - 1$ and **E** $y = 5x - 4$ *(1 mark each)*

12. a) Number 8   b) Number 9
   c) B   d) A = 2.73   B = 2.85   *(1 mark each)*

13. $\frac{3}{5}, \frac{5}{8}, \frac{7}{10}, \frac{3}{4}, \frac{17}{20}$ *(1 mark)*

14. a)   *(1 mark)*

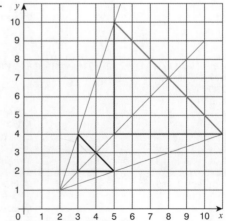

   b) 32 cm²   *(1 mark for number, 1 for units)*
   c) 12   *(1 mark)*

15. $\frac{1}{8}, \frac{1}{4}, \frac{3}{8}, \frac{5}{8}, 1, 1\frac{5}{8}$ *(3 marks: 1 for each term)*

16. a) yes, 150, 165   b) no, 175, 185
   c) weak positive   *(1 mark each)*

Paper 11

1. A and C   B and E   *(3 marks: 2 if three correct,*
   D and F   G and H (in any order)   *1 if two correct)*

2. a) 44.764 cm²   *(1 mark for number, 1 for unit)*
   b) 23.56   *(1 mark)*

3. a) B   1 1 1 2 2 2 3 3 3   *(2 marks: 1 if just*
     W   1 2 3 1 2 3 1 2 3   *one omission)*
   b) (i) 4
     (ii) $\frac{6}{9}$ or $\frac{2}{3}$ *(1 mark each)*

4.

Smaller triangle drawn
Enlargement of triangle
Centre of enlargement at (2, 1)   *(1 mark each)*

5. $-2\,°C$ $\quad$ $0\,°C$ $\quad$ $5\,°C$ $\hfill$ *(1 mark)*
$\quad$ (In any order)
6. a) 8
$\quad$ b) 7 $\hfill$ *(1 mark each)*
7. 16.6 $\hfill$ *(2 marks: 1 for answer in range (16 to 17))*
8. 6 $\hfill$ *(1 mark)*
9. 48 m³ $\hfill$ *(1 mark for number, 1 for units)*
10. 5% cheaper by £31 $\hfill$ *(1 mark)*
11. $\frac{4}{5}$ $\hfill$ *(1 mark)*
12. a) $9x$
$\quad$ b) $9x + 5$
$\quad$ c) $9x + 5 = 4(x + 5)$
$\quad$ d) 27 and 3 $\hfill$ *(1 mark each)*
13. a)

x	0	1	2
y	1	3	5

$\quad$ b)

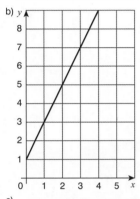

$\quad$ c)

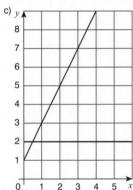

$\quad$ d) $(\frac{1}{2}, 2)$ $\hfill$ *(1 mark each)*
14. $a = 75°$
$\quad$ $b = 110°$
$\quad$ $c = 35°$ $\hfill$ *(1 mark each)*
15. £16 $\hfill$ *(1 mark)*
16. 5 $\quad$ 8 $\quad$ 11 $\hfill$ *(1 mark)*
17. AB = in range (7.1 to 7.5) cm
$\quad$ AC = in range (8.8 to 9.2) cm $\hfill$ *(1 mark each)*
18. a) $c = 2s + 2$
$\quad$ b) 49 $\hfill$ *(1 mark each)*

Paper 12
1. (20, 0) $\hfill$ *(1 mark)*
2. Between 5.47 cm and 5.48 $\hfill$ *(1 mark each)*
3. a) 4 $\hfill$ b) $4n$
$\quad$ c) n^2 or $n \times n$
$\quad$ d) $n^2 + 4n + 4$ $\quad$ or $\quad$ $n \times n + 4n + 4$ $\hfill$ *(1 mark each)*
4. 25% $\hfill$ *(1 mark)*
5. a) 9
$\quad$ b) 8
$\quad$ c) 4 $\hfill$ *(1 mark each)*

6. a) B $\quad$ b) E $\quad$ c) D $\quad$ d) A $\quad$ e) C $\hfill$ *(4 marks: 1 for each correct then −1 from total)*
7. $1 \times 1 \times 72$ $\quad$ $2 \times 3 \times 12$
$\quad$ $1 \times 2 \times 36$ $\quad$ $2 \times 6 \times 6$
$\quad$ $2 \times 9 \times 4$ etc… $\hfill$ *(3 marks: 1 each for any three)*
8. a) 1 : 9
$\quad$ b) The scale factor is 3 with centre of enlargement at (2, 2) $\hfill$ *(1 mark each)*
9. a)

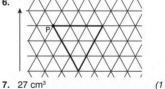

$\quad$ b) 1064 $\hfill$ *(1 mark each)*
10. 30° $\hfill$ *(1 mark)*
11. a) 82.5
$\quad$ b) 18 $\hfill$ *(1 mark each)*
12. 47 $\hfill$ *(1 mark)*
13. Above $\quad$ (3, 3) $\hfill$ *(2 marks: 1 mark if*
$\quad$ On $\quad$ (1, 0) $\quad$ (2, 1) $\quad$ (3, 2) $\hfill$ *one or two lines*
$\quad$ Below $\quad$ (3, 1) $\quad$ (4, 2) $\hfill$ *wrong)*
14.

$\times$	$\frac{1}{2}$	$\frac{1}{4}$	$\frac{1}{3}$	$\frac{2}{3}$
2	1	$\frac{1}{2}$	$\frac{2}{3}$	$1\frac{1}{3}$
3	$1\frac{1}{2}$	$\frac{3}{1}$	1	2
5	$2\frac{1}{2}$	$1\frac{1}{4}$	$1\frac{2}{3}$	$3\frac{1}{3}$

$\hfill$ *(4 marks: 1 for each correct cell)*
15. $C = \frac{F}{2} - 15$ $\hfill$ *(1 mark)*
16. a) Black 1 $\quad$ 1 $\quad$ 1 $\quad$ 2 $\quad$ 2 $\quad$ 2
$\quad\quad$ Grey $\quad$ 1 $\quad$ 2 $\quad$ 3 $\quad$ 1 $\quad$ 2 $\quad$ 3 $\hfill$ *(1 mark)*
$\quad$ (in any order)
$\quad$ b) $\frac{4}{6}$ or $\frac{2}{3}$ $\hfill$ *(1 mark)*
17. a)

Height (cm)	Frequency
140 to 149	2
150 to 159	8
160 to 169	14
170 to 179	6

$\hfill$ *(2 marks: 1 if one error in a frequency cell)*
$\quad$ b) 10 $\hfill$ *(1 mark)*
18. 6 cm² $\hfill$ *(1 mark)*

Paper 13
1. a) 2.5
$\quad$ b) 7 $\hfill$ *(1 mark each)*
2. −10 and −11 $\hfill$ *(1 mark)*
3. Sanjay is right, there are about 5000 grains of salt on a teaspoon. $\hfill$ *(1 mark)*
4. a) 16 $\hfill$ b) 10 $\hfill$ *(1 mark each)*
5. £72.50 $\hfill$ *(1 mark)*
6.

Logo	Order of rotation symmetry	Number of lines of symmetry	Logo	Order of rotation symmetry	Number of lines of symmetry
A	0	1	C	4	0
B	2	0	D	4	4

$\hfill$ *(3 marks: 1 for each line of correct direction and length)*
7. 27 cm³ $\hfill$ *(1 mark for number, 1 for units)*
8. $\hfill$ *(3 marks: 2 if 6 or 7 cells correct; 1 if 5 cells correct)*

9. a) **2**

b)
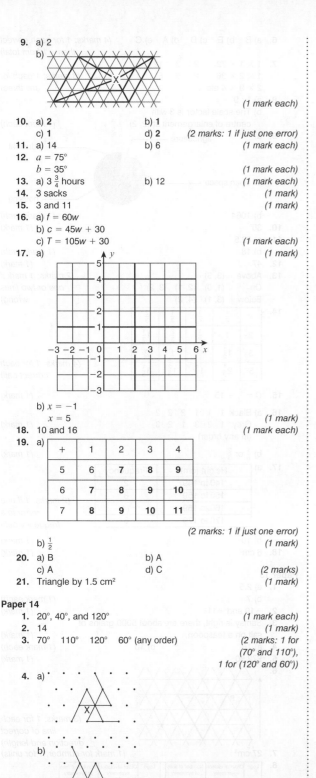

(1 mark each)

10. a) **2**   b) **1**

c) **1**   d) **2**   *(2 marks: 1 if just one error)*

11. a) 14   b) 6   *(1 mark each)*

12. $a = 75°$

$b = 35°$ *(1 mark each)*

13. a) $3\frac{3}{4}$ hours   b) 12   *(1 mark each)*

14. 3 sacks   *(1 mark)*

15. 3 and 11   *(1 mark)*

16. a) $f = 60w$

b) $c = 45w + 30$

c) $T = 105w + 30$ *(1 mark each)*

17. a)   *(1 mark)*

<!-- graph grid with y axis from -3 to 5 and x axis from -3 to 6 -->

b) $x = -1$

$x = 5$ *(1 mark)*

18. 10 and 16   *(1 mark each)*

19. a)

+	1	2	3	4
5	6	**7**	8	9
6	**7**	8	9	10
7	**8**	9	10	11

(2 marks: 1 if just one error)

b) $\frac{1}{2}$ *(1 mark)*

20. a) B   b) A

c) A   d) C   *(2 marks)*

21. Triangle by 1.5 cm²   *(1 mark)*

Paper 14

1. 20°, 40°, and 120°   *(1 mark each)*

2. 14   *(1 mark)*

3. 70°   110°   120°   60° (any order)   *(2 marks: 1 for (70° and 110°), 1 for (120° and 60°))*

4. a)

<!-- dot grid reflection figure with X -->

b)

<!-- dot grid reflection figure with X -->

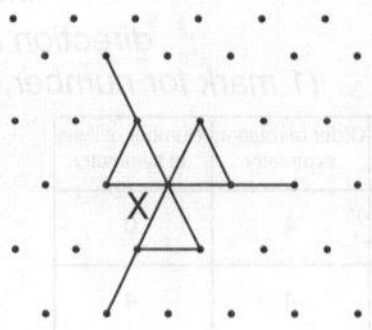

(1 mark each)

5. 19   *(1 mark)*

6. a) Between 4 and 5

b) Between 4.9 and 5.0   *(1 mark each)*

---

7. 10   *(1 mark)*

8. a) scale factor 2

b)

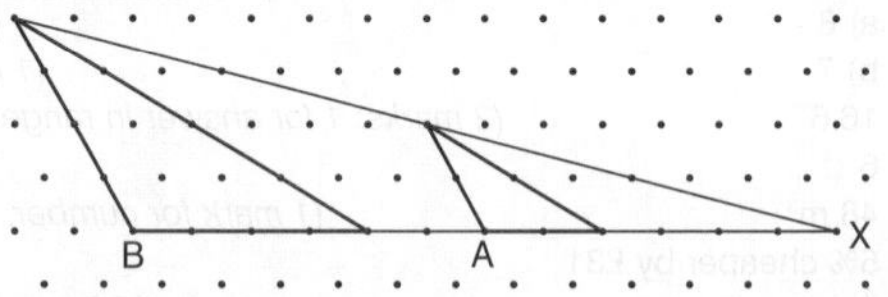

<!-- dot grid triangles labelled B, A, X -->

(1 mark each)

9. 75% of 420 m by 7 m   *(1 mark)*

10. a) 6

b) $\frac{11}{3}$ or $3\frac{2}{3}$

c) 5

d) 3   *(1 mark each)*

11. $a = 50°$

$b = 130°$

$c = 130°$ *(1 mark each)*

12. a) $3n$

b) $4n$

c) $100 = 4n + 6n$ or $10n = 100$

30 ducks   10 cows   *(4 marks: 1 mark each)*

13. $y = 3x$ **1**

$y = 2x$ **3**

$y = x$ **5**

$y = x + 1$ **4**

$y = 2x + 1$ **2**   *(2 marks: 1 one or two errors)*

14.

÷	$\frac{1}{4}$	$\frac{1}{3}$	$\frac{3}{4}$	$\frac{2}{3}$
3	12	9	4	$2\frac{1}{4}$
4	16	12	$5\frac{1}{3}$	6
5	20	**15**	$6\frac{2}{3}$	$7\frac{1}{2}$

(4 marks: 1 for each correct cell)

15. a) 16 possible combinations, in any order:

12   14   16   18

32   34   36   38

52   54   56   58

72   74   76   78   *(2 marks: 1 if one or two errors)*

b) $\frac{3}{16}$ *(1 mark)*

16. Kite, arrowhead   *(1 mark)*

17. a) 5

b) Joss

c) Joss by $\frac{1}{2}$ an hour

d) 1pm, 2:30pm, 3:30pm   *(1 mark each)*

Paper 15

1. a) $5x = 30$ *(1 mark)*

b) 10 cm, 2 cm, 6 cm   *(2 marks: 1 if two correct)*

2. $w = 61°$

$x = 47°$

$y = 133°$

$z = 47°$ *(1 mark each)*

3. A = grey

B = white

C = grey

D = white   *(2 marks: 1 if just one error)*

4. RT 30   FD 2

RT 120   FD 1

RT 60   FD 1

RT 240   FD 1

RT 120   FD 2

RT 120   FD 2   *(3 marks: 2 if three correct lines, 1 if two correct lines)*

5. a) $n = 9$

b) $n = 4$

c) $n = 6$ *(1 mark each)*

6. a) Reflection in the y-axis
b) 90° clockwise rotation about origin
c) Translation 5 to the right and 2 down
d) Rotation $\frac{1}{2}$ turn about origin OR reflect in x-axis then reflect in y-axis.
e) Reflection in x-axis *(1 mark each)*

7. 6%, $12\frac{1}{2}$%, $33\frac{1}{3}$%, 0.45, $\frac{3}{5}$, 0.68, $\frac{7}{10}$, $\frac{4}{5}$ *(1 mark)*

8. nitre 3000 g charcoal 600 g
sulphur 400 g *(2 marks: 1 if two correct)*

9. a) 2.5 b) 2.4
c) 6 d) 3 *(1 mark each)*

10. £7.44 *(1 mark)*

11. a) $x^2 + 7x$ b) 17 m *(1 mark each)*

12. a) $3n$ b) $25n$ (or $10n + 15n$)
c) 60 5p coins   20 10p coins *(1 mark each)*

13. $y = 2x$ A
$y = 2x + 5$ C
$y = 3x - 1$ E
$y = -x$ B   *(3 marks: 2 for four*
$y = -2x - 3$ F   *correct, 1 for three correct)*

14. a) $\frac{2}{3} \times 9 = 6$ b) $2 \div \frac{1}{3} = 6$
c) $\frac{1}{3} \times 6 = 2$ d) $6 \div \frac{2}{3} = 9$ *(1 mark each)*

Paper 16

1. a) 0730 b) 15 minutes / $\frac{1}{4}$ of an hour
c) 140 miles *(1 mark each)*

2. a) Any percentage between 80% and 90% but not including either.
b) Any decimal between 0.26 and 0.3 but not including either. *(1 mark each)*

3. $\frac{3}{4}$ *(1 mark)*

4. a) 11 g b) 55%
c) Mixture A *(1 mark each)*

5. $a = 50°$ $b = 50°$ *(1 mark each)*

6. 35° 35° 145° 145° *(1 mark)*

7. a) square, rectangle, rhombus, parallelogram
b) square, kite, arrowhead, rhombus
c) Arrowhead, kite *(1 mark each)*

8. C and D *(1 mark)*

9. a)

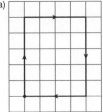

b) FD 3   RT 90
FD 3   RT 90
FD 3   RT 90
FD 3 *(1 mark each)*

10. 3.4 *(2 marks: 1 for answer between 3.3 and 3.5)*

11. C, B, D, A *(2 marks: 1 for cheapest and most expensive correct)*

12. a)

×	1	2	3	4
second dice				
1	1	2	3	4
2	2	4	6	8
3	3	6	9	12
4	4	8	12	16

(first dice on left axis)

b) 4
c) $\frac{2}{16}$ or $\frac{1}{8}$
d) 7 different scores are possible:
2, 3, 4, 5, 6, 7 and 8 *(1 mark each)*

13. a) $11\frac{1}{4}$ hours b) £8 *(1 mark each)*

14. a) $x = 7$ b) $x = 150$ c) $x = 6$ *(1 mark each)*

15.

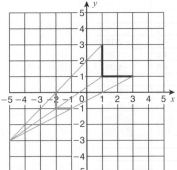

a) 1 mark for small "L"
b) 1 mark for × 2 enlargement of small "L" *(1 mark each)*

16. a)

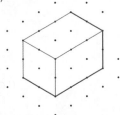

b) 12 cm³ c) 32 cm² *(1 mark each)*

17. a) 3.72 m b) 1.116 m² *(1 mark each)*

18. a) 12 b) $3n$ *(1 mark each)*

Paper 17

1. Jason: 20 and Safiq: 40 *(1 mark)*

2. 4 cm² *(1 mark)*

3. a) 75° b) 15° *(1 mark each)*

4. a) 1220 kg
b) 1.22 tonne *(1 mark each)*

5. a) $(P =) 7x + 28$ *(2 marks: 1 for each term)*
b) 7 m *(1 mark)*

6. a) £21 b) £21 *(1 mark each)*

7. $1 \to B$ $2 \to D$ or A *(2 marks: 1*
$3 \to D$ or A $4 \to E$ $5 \to C$ *if four correct)*

8. 14 different possible answers:
2, 3, 4, 5, 6, 7, 8, 9, 10, 11, 12, 14, 16, 18 *(2 marks)*

9. 2 and 3 are parallel *(1 mark)*

10. $\frac{1}{25}$ *(1 mark)*

11. a) 3   5   7   9
b) $T(n) = 2n + 1$ *(1 mark each)*

12. 18.75 cm² *(1 mark)*

13. 125° *(1 mark)*

14. No, the house price has gone up $3x$ (not $2x$) *(1 mark)*

15. LT 90   FD 4   LT 90   FD 1
LT 90   FD 3   RT 90   FD 1 *(2 marks)*

16. -6 °C *(1 mark)*

17. a) $37\frac{1}{2}$ kg b) 160 *(1 mark each)*

18. a) $x = 3$ b) $y = 8$ c) $x = 36$ *(1 mark each)*

19. a) reflection in the y-axis *(4 marks: $\frac{1}{2}$ for each*
b) 2 maps onto 4 ... *correct, round total down)*
c) 2 maps onto 5 ...
d) ... rotation 90° clockwise, centre $(-3, -3)$
e) ... by reflection in the line BD
f) ... reflection in the y-axis
g) ... translation 7 units to the right and 6 units down (6 down then 7 to the right)
h) ... reflection in the y-axis

20.

◇	A	B
1	x	x^2-19
2	3	−10
3	4	3
4	5	6
5	4.1	**−2.19**
6	4.5	1.25
7	4.2	**−1.36**
8	4.3	−0.51
9	4.4	0.36
10	4.35	−0.0775
11	4.36	0.0096
12	4.37	0.0969
13		
14		
15		
16		

4.4 *(2 marks)*

21. 99.5% *(1 mark)*

22.

1	$\frac{3}{10}$	$\frac{19}{20}$
$\frac{7}{10}$	$\frac{3}{4}$	$\frac{4}{5}$
$\frac{11}{10}$	$1\frac{1}{5}$	$\frac{1}{2}$

(1 mark each)

Paper 18

1. 100°   40°   40°
isosceles *(1 mark for angles, 1 mark for triangle name)*

2. a) $x = 3$ b) $x = 12$ *(1 mark each)*

3. 166.5 cm   *(2 marks: 1 for 126.5)*

4. $a = 135°$
$b = 65°$
$c = 70°$ *(1 mark each)*

5. Any three equations passing through (1, 1)
e.g. $y = 1, x = 1, y = x, y = 2x - 1$, etc.   *(1 mark)*

6.   *(1 mark)*

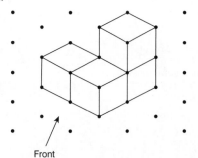

Front

7. a) $\frac{5}{6}$ $\frac{6}{7}$
b) $\frac{n}{n + 1}$ *(1 mark each)*

8. 16   *(1 mark)*

9. a) Either $x = 10$ or $x = 1$
b) $x = 5$ *(1 mark each)*

10. 36 m   *(1 mark)*

11. a) 50 m
b) Amber
c) Amber
d) Amber for 10 seconds   *(1 mark each)*

12. 864 litres   *(2 marks: 1 for 864000)*

13. 37% $\frac{3}{8}$ 0.4   42% $\frac{3}{7}$ 0.43   *(1 mark)*

14. $a = 1\frac{1}{4}$
$b = 7\frac{1}{8}$ *(1 mark each)*

15. $22\frac{1}{2}$ cm²   *(2 marks: 1 for 25)*

16. $a = 235°$
$b = 70°$ *(1 mark each)*

17. RT 60   FD 1   RT 300   FD 1   LIFT
RT 60   FD 1   DROP   FD 1   *(2 marks)*

18. a) No, 182 cm for person and 173 cm for friend
b) No, 162 cm for person and 158 cm for friend
c) No correlation   *(1 mark each)*

19. a) Translation 2 units to right and 2 units up
b) Rotation 90° clockwise about (1, 4)
c) Enlargement, scale factor 2, with centre of
   enlargement at (1, 7)   *(1 mark each)*

20. Above: A E G
On: B D
Below: C F   *(2 marks: 1 for one or more correct grouping)*

14. a) Complete this drawing of a cuboid.

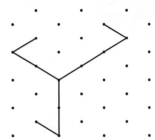

b) (i) The cuboid measures 2 cm by 3 cm by 2 cm.
What is the total area of the cuboid?

_____ _____

(ii) What is the volume of the cuboid?

_____ cm³

/4

15. The term-to-term rule for the sequence below is "add the two previous terms"

1   5   6   11   17   ...

This sequence has the same term-to-term rule.
Find the missing terms.

_____ $\frac{1}{4}$ $\frac{3}{8}$ _____   1   _____

/3

16. This scatter graph shows the heights of pairs of adult brothers and sisters from 10 different families. The measurements were intended to see if there was any connection between brothers' and sisters' heights.

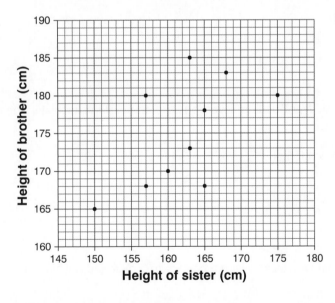

Height of sister (cm)

a) Is the shortest sister from the same family as the shortest brother (yes or no)?

_____

Shortest sister's height _____ cm

Shortest brother's height _____ cm

b) Are the tallest brother and sister from the same family (yes or no)? _____

Tallest sister's height

_____ cm

Tallest brother's height

_____ cm

/3

c) Which of these statements best describes the correlation between brothers' and sisters' heights in the scatter graph? Circle the correct answer.

Strong positive   Weak positive   Strong negative

Weak negative   No correlation

/40

PAPER 11

1. This pair of solids will fit together to make a cube.

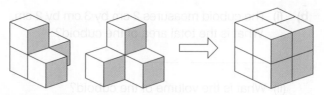

Pair up these solids to make four more cubes of the same size.

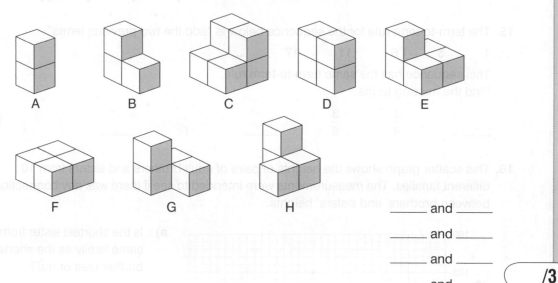

| A | B | C | D | E |

| F | G | H |

_____ and _____

_____ and _____

_____ and _____

_____ and _____ /3

2. The clock-faces on the Royal Liver Building, Liverpool, are some of the largest in the world. The diameter of each clock face is 7.6 m.

   a) What is the area of one clock face? (Take $\pi = 3.1$) _____

   b) How far does the tip of the minute hand travel in one hour? (Assume that it extends to the edge of the clock face.) _____ m /3

3. Pete works as an assistant child-minder.
   He has invented a game that involves throwing a black 1 to 3 dice and a white 1 to 3 dice, and adding their scores.

   a) List all the possible outcomes when the numbers on each dice are added.

   b) (i) Which is the most likely score? _____

   (ii) What is the probability of **not** getting the most likely score? _____ /4

4. Draw an enlargement scale factor 3 and centre of enlargement (2, 1) of the triangle whose vertices are at (3, 4), (5, 2) and (3, 2).

Leave all your construction lines and the original triangle in.

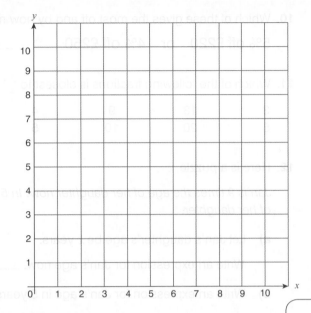

/3

5. The mean of three temperatures is 1 °C. The median temperature is 0 °C, and the range of the three temperatures is 7 °C.

What are the three temperatures? _____°C _____°C _____°C

/1

6. Solve these equations.

a) $a - 2 = 6$ $a =$ _____   b) $2b + 3 = 17$ $b =$ _____

/2

7. Using trial and improvement, solve this 4000-year-old puzzle.
A number and a seventh of that number together make 19. What is the number?

Give your answer to 1 decimal place. _____

/2

8. How many $\frac{2}{3}$ litre bottles can be filled from a 4 litre bucket? _____

/1

9. Here is a net for a cuboid.

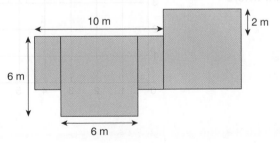

10 m   2 m   6 m   6 m

What is the cuboid's volume? _____ _____

/2

10. Which of these gives the most off and by how much?

5% off £220   or   4% off £250 _____ by   £ _____

/1

11. Which of the following fractions is closest to $\frac{3}{4}$?

$\frac{3}{5}$ $\frac{13}{20}$ $\frac{9}{10}$ $\frac{4}{5}$ $\frac{19}{20}$ _____

/1

12. Here is a puzzle.

Jan is 9 times the age of her daughter now. In 5 years' time Jan will only be 4 times the age of her daughter.

a) Let Jan's daughter's age be x years.

Write an expression for Jan's age now. _____

b) Write an expression for Jan's age in 5 years' time. _____

c) Write an equation that shows that Jan's age in 5 years' time will be 4 times her daughter's age in 5 years' time. _____

d) Solve the equation to find both their ages now.

Jan is _____ and her daughter is _____

/4

13. a) Complete this table of values for $y = 2x + 1$

x	0	1	2
y	___	___	___

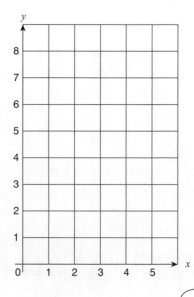

b) Draw the graph of $y = 2x + 1$ on this grid.

c) On the grid draw the straight line $x = 2$.

d) Write the coordinates of the point where the two lines intersect.

(___ , ___)

/4

14. Calculate the angles marked with letters.

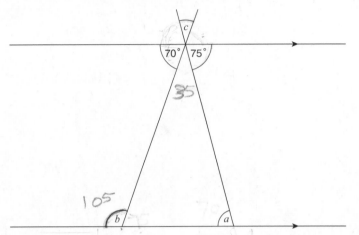

$a =$ ___75___ °

$b =$ ___110___ °

$c =$ ___35___ °

/3

15. A television costs £576. Maxine pays a deposit of one third of the cost. She pays the rest in 24 equal monthly instalments. Work out how much she pays each month.

£ _____

/1

16. Write the first three terms of the sequence whose nth term, T(n), is $3n + 2$

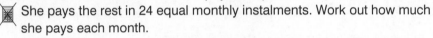

/1

17. This is a sketch of a triangle.
On a separate sheet of paper draw the triangle accurately and measure the length of the sides AB and AC.

AB = _____ cm

AC = _____ cm

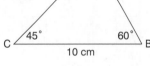

/2

18. Here is a pattern of squares and circles

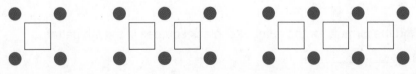

a) Find a rule connecting the number of squares, s, with the number of circles, c.

_____

/2

b) How many squares will there be if there are 100 circles?

_____

/40

PAPER 12

1.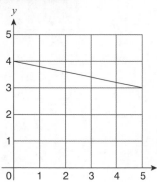

Work out the coordinates of the point where this straight line cuts the x-axis.

(_____ , _____)

2. A square has an area of 30 cm².

Working to 2 decimal places, find between which lengths the side of the square lies.

Between _____ cm and _____ cm

3. Black, grey and white tiles are arranged to make a sequence.

These are the first three patterns.

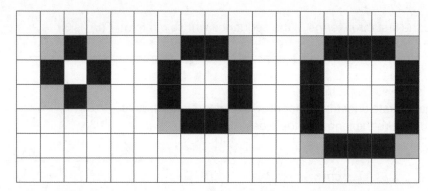

a) Find the formula for the number of grey squares in the nth pattern.

$G =$ _____

b) Find the formula for the number of black squares in the nth pattern.

$B =$ _____

c) Find the formula for the number of white squares in the nth pattern.

$W =$ _____

d) Find the formula for the total number of squares in the nth pattern.

$T =$ _____

4. Red gold is made from gold and copper. It contains 3 times as much gold as copper.

   What is the percentage of copper in red gold? _____%

   /1

5. Solve these equations.

   a) $2x + 1 = 19$ $x =$ _____

   b) $\dfrac{x}{2} = 4$ $x =$ _____

   c) $3(x + 2) = 18$ $x =$ _____

   /3

6. Match the directions of viewing on this model with the views shown below.

   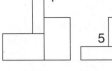

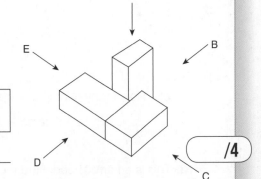

   a) _____   **b)** _____   **c)** _____   **d)** _____   **e)** _____

   /4

7. Lorna has 72 one centimetre cubes.
   Write the dimensions of 3 different shaped cuboids, volume 72 cm³, which she can make from them.

   a) _____ cm   by _____ cm   by _____ cm

   b) _____ cm   by _____ cm   by _____ cm

   c) _____ cm   by _____ cm   by _____ cm

   /3

8. One small square on this grid represents 1 cm².

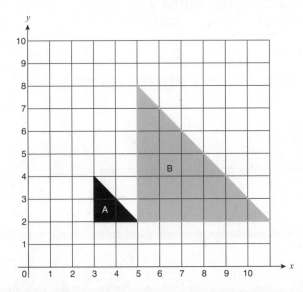

   a) What is the ratio of the area of the black triangle to the area of the grey triangle? (Give your answer as a simple ratio.)

   _____ : _____

   b) Triangle B is an enlargement of triangle A.

   The scale factor is

   _____ with centre of enlargement at

   (_____ , _____)

   /3

9. A large town covers 4838 hectares. Of this area, 20% is industrial land, 49% is housing, 22% is open space and the rest is agricultural land.

   a) Label this pie chart to fit these percentages.

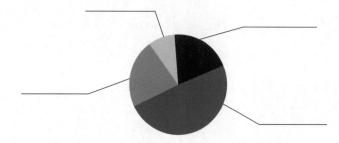

   b) How many hectares of open space is there to the nearest hectare?

   _____ hectares

   /2

10. This is an arrowhead. Find the value of x.

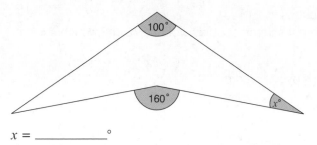

   $x =$ _____ °

   /1

11. The biggest Ferris wheel in the world is the Singapore Flyer.
    It is 165 m in diameter. There are 28 pods around its circumference.

    a) What is the radius of the big wheel? _____ m

    b) What is the distance, to the nearest metre, between pods on the wheel's circumference?

    (Take $\pi = 3.1$) _____ m

    /2

12. Find the smallest whole number which gives an answer greater than 100000

    when it is cubed. _____

    /1

13. Which of these points are above the line $y = x - 1$, which are below it and which are on it?

(1, 0)   (3, 1)   (2, 1)   (3, 2)   (3, 3)   (4, 2)

above _____

on   _____

below _____

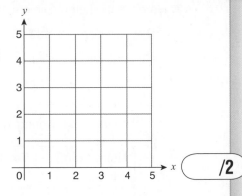

/2

14. Complete this multiplication grid.

×	$\frac{1}{2}$	$\frac{1}{4}$	_____	$\frac{2}{3}$
2	1	$\frac{1}{2}$	$\frac{2}{3}$	_____
3	_____	$\frac{3}{4}$	1	2
5	$2\frac{1}{2}$	$1\frac{1}{4}$	$1\frac{2}{3}$	_____

/4

15. Here is a rough rule for changing a temperature in degrees Fahrenheit into degrees Celsius.

> Divide the Fahrenheit temperature by two and subtract 15.

Write this as a formula connecting C, temperature in Celsius, and F, temperature in Fahrenheit.

_____

/1

16. Here are two sets of number cards, one grey and the other black.

One card is taken at random from each set.

a) List all the possible outcomes. _____

b) What is the probability that the two numbers are different? _____

/2

17. Here are the heights, in cm, of a group of students.

154	167	163	148	143	169	155	179	153	173
167	164	151	160	172	160	161	150	164	178
156	155	165	152	164	166	163	170	172	169

a) Put these heights into a completed grouped frequency table starting at 140 cm with each interval covering 10 cm.

Height (cm)	Tally	Frequency
140 to		

b) How many students were less than 160 cm tall? _____

/3

18. This triangle is drawn on a piece of centimetre squared paper.

Calculate the area of the triangle. _____ cm²

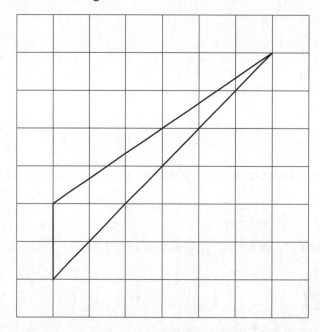

/1

/40

PAPER 13

1. Solve each of these equations.

   a) $5x = 10 + x$ $x =$ _____

   b) $\dfrac{35}{x} = 5$ $x =$ _____

   /2

2. The sum of two consecutive numbers is -21.

   What are the two numbers? _____ and _____

   /1

3. Grains of salt are roughly cubic with sides 1 mm. A teaspoon holds about 5 cm³ of salt.
   Sanjay says that a teaspoon can hold over 1000 grains of salt.
   Is he right? Calculate the answer.

   Sanjay is _____, there are about _____ grains of salt in a teaspoon.

   /1

4. The length, l cm, of a spring is connected to the load, m kg, on its end by the formula:

$$l = \frac{m}{4} + 10$$

   a) A load of 24 kg is attached to the spring. What is the length of the spring?

       _____ cm

   b) What is the length of the spring without a load?

       _____ cm

   /2

5. A digital camera costs £325 cash. It can be bought for a deposit of 30% of the price and
   12 monthly payments of £25.
   How much more does it cost to buy the camera this way?

   £ _____

   /1

6. Here are two types of commands for moving a model turtle.

> FD 10 means move forward 10 cm
>
> RT 30 means turn 30° clockwise

On this 1 cm triangle paper draw the shape drawn by these commands.
Start at point P with the turtle facing up the page in the direction of the arrow.

RT 90   FD 3   RT 120   FD 3   RT 120   FD 3

/3

7. The surface area of a cube is 54 cm². What is its volume?

_____

/2

8. Complete the table describing fully the symmetry of each of these logos.

     A   B   C   D

Logo	Order of rotational symmetry	Number of lines of symmetry	Logo	Order of rotational symmetry	Number of lines of symmetry
A			C		
B			D		

/3

9. A'B'C'D' is an enlargement of the parallelogram ABCD.

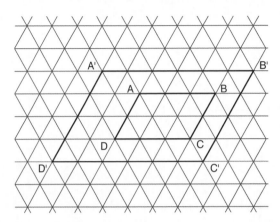

a) What is the scale factor of the enlargement?

_____

b) Find the centre of enlargement and mark it with a cross.

/2

10. Which is the greater in each of these pairs?

 a) **1** 25% of 3.6 m   or   **2** 5% of 20 m   _____

b) **1** 50% of 75 km   or   **2** 10% of 370 km   _____

c) **1** 10% of 125 kg   or   **2** 75% of 16 kg   _____

d) **1** 15% of £5   or   **2** 10% of £8   _____

/2

11. Solve these equations.

a) $4(x + 1) = 3(x + 6)$ $x =$ _____

b) $5x - 2 = 3x + 10$ $x =$ _____

/2

12. Calculate the angles marked with letters.

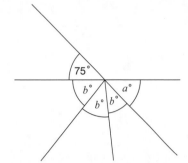

$a =$ _____ °

$b =$ _____ °

/2

13. Donna is a hairdresser. It takes her $\frac{3}{4}$ of an hour to tint a customer's hair.

a) At this rate how long will it take her to tint 5 customers' hair? _____ hours

b) If she worked non-stop in a tinting marathon for charity, how many customers' hair could she tint in 9 hours? _____

/2

14. A grass roundabout is roughly circular with a radius of about 30 m.
50 g of grass seed will cover a square metre.
How many 50 kg sacks of grass seed will be needed to seed the roundabout?

(Take $\pi = 3.1$) _____ sacks

/1

15. Find two whole numbers less than 20 so that when you divide one number by the other, the answer is 0.27272727 _____ and _____

/1

16. An old rule used to give the time for cooking a turkey is:

• Cook for 45 minutes per kilo, plus an extra 30 minutes.
• To defrost a frozen turkey, by putting it in cold water to get it ready for cooking, allow 60 minutes per kilo.

a) Use the second rule above to write a formula connecting the **defrosting time**, f, in minutes with the weight of the turkey, w, in kilos. _____

b) Write another formula linking the **cooking time**, c, in minutes, with the turkey's weight, w, in kilos. _____

c) Write another formula connecting the time, from removing the turkey from the freezer till ready to remove from oven, T minutes, with the weight in kilos, w, of the turkey.

_____

/3

17. a) On the grid draw the lines
$x = 2$, $y = 1$ and $y = 4$

b) Write the possible equations
of the fourth straight line
which will form a square.

_____

_____

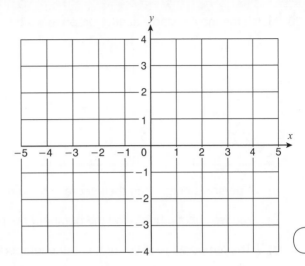

/2

18. Find two numbers that are in the sequence beginning

4   7   10   13   ...

and also in the sequence whose nth term is $2n + 6$.

_____ and _____

/2

19. Here are two fair spinners.
The numbers shown by the arrow on each spinner
are added to give the total.

a) Complete this table showing all the possible
outcomes and totals.

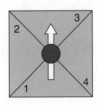
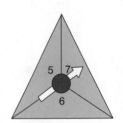

+	1	2	3	4
5	6			
6				
7				

/3

b) What is the probability of getting a total of 8 or less? _____

20. Match the most suitable scatter graph to each of the questions below.

A
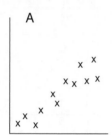

B
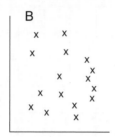

C
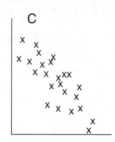

a) A person's height and their score in a maths test. _____

b) The weight of a book and the number of pages in it. _____

c) The temperature in London and the temperature in Birmingham. _____

d) The price of a car and its age. _____

/2

21. This triangle and parallelogram are drawn on centimetre square paper. Which has the greater area and by how much?

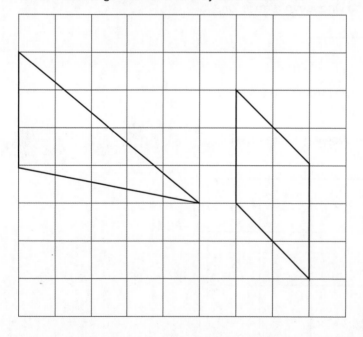

_____ by _____ cm²

/1

/40

PAPER 14

1. The three angles of a triangle are in the ratio 1 : 2 : 6.

   Find the size of each angle. _____° _____° _____°

   /3

2. If the nth term of a sequence T(n) is given by $7(n + 1)$, what number term is the first to be greater than 100? _____

   /1

3. Which four of these angles could be the internal angles of a trapezium?

   10°   30°   60°   70°   100°   110°   120°

   _____° _____° _____° _____°

   /2

4. Complete these drawings so that each one has a 3-fold rotation centre at X.

   a)

   b)

   /2

5. This is a diagram of an iron gate.

   Using $\pi = 3$, calculate the approximate length of iron rod needed to make the gate.

   _____ m

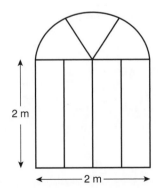

   /1

6. In the equation $n \times (n + 1) \times (n + 2) = 200$:

    a) find between which two whole numbers n must lie.

    Between _____ and _____

    b) Find between which two 1 decimal place numbers n must lie,
    (e.g. between 1.4 and 1.5).

    Between _____ and _____

/2

7. These are two views of the same solid, which is made from centimetre cubes.

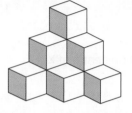 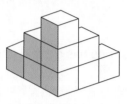

What is the volume of the solid?

_____ cm^3

/1

8. Triangle A is transformed into triangle B by an enlargement.

    a) What is the scale factor of the enlargement?

    _____

    b) Mark the centre of enlargement with a cross.

/2

9. Which is longer, and by how much:

75% of 420 m or 35% of 880 m?

_____ by _____ m

/1

10. Solve these equations.

    a) $2x + 5 = x + 11$ $x =$ _____

    b) $3x = 11$ $x =$ _____

    c) $4 = \dfrac{20}{x}$ $x =$ _____

    d) $3(x - 1) + 5(x + 2) = 31$ $x =$ _____

11. Find the size of the lettered angles.

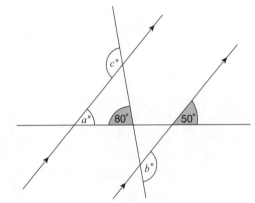

$a =$ _____ $^{\circ}$

$b =$ _____ $^{\circ}$

$c =$ _____ $^{\circ}$

12. Here is part of a puzzle from a Victorian maths book.

> **Jerome keeps ducks and cows. He has three times as many ducks as cows.
> All these animals together have a total of 100 legs.**

    a)   If Jerome has n cows, how many ducks does he have? _____

    b)   How many legs do the n cows have? _____

    c)   Write down and solve an equation to find the number of ducks and cows Jerome has.

    _____

        number of ducks _____   number of cows _____

13. Match each equation with its line.

$y = 3x$ _____

$y = 2x$ _____

$y = x$ _____

$y = x + 1$ _____

$y = 2x + 1$ _____

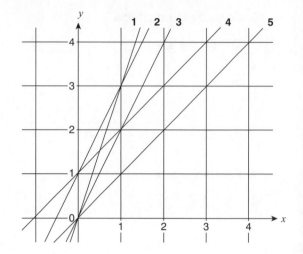

14. Complete this division grid.

/2

÷	$\frac{1}{4}$	$\frac{1}{3}$	$\frac{3}{4}$	$\frac{2}{3}$
3	12	___	4	$2\frac{1}{4}$
4	16	12	___	6
5	20	___	$6\frac{2}{3}$	___

/4

15. Toya has a locker. It has a simple combination lock.
The first dial has the odd numbers 1, 3, 5 and 7 on it.
The second dial has the even numbers 2, 4, 6 and 8 on it.

a) Show all the possible combinations. How many are there?

_____

_____ combinations

b) Toya forgets her combination, but she knows that it makes a number that 12 (her lucky number) goes into exactly. She tries one of these numbers that 12 goes into exactly. What is the probability that it is the correct one?

_____

/3

16. Which quadrilaterals have diagonals that cut at right angles and only have one line of symmetry?

/1

_____

17. Here are the distance–time graphs of two walkers on a 10-mile hike.

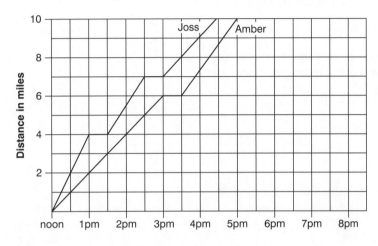

a) How long did it take Amber to finish the hike?

_____ hours

b) Who was fastest over the first 3 miles?

_____

c) Who rested the most and by how much more?

_____

d) At what times were they furthest apart?

_____

/4

/40

PAPER 15

1. The perimeter of this quadrilateral is 28 cm.

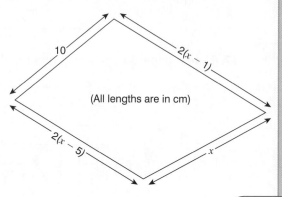

(All lengths are in cm)

   a) Use the information in the diagram to set up an equation involving x.

      _____

   b) By solving your equation find the lengths of the three sides not given.

      _____ cm

      _____ cm

      _____ cm

/3

2. Calculate the values of w, x, y and z.

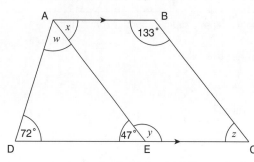

$w =$ _____ °

$x =$ _____ °

$y =$ _____ °

$z =$ _____ °

/4

3. This skeleton cube is made from wire.
At each corner or vertex is a ball.
The balls are either black, white or grey.

Write down the colour of the lettered balls in these views.

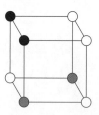

  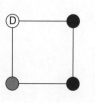

A _____   B _____   C _____   D _____

/2

4. Here are two types of commands for moving a model turtle.

FD 10 means move forward 10 cm

RT 30 means turn 30° clockwise

Starting from A, write the commands to draw
this polygon on 1 cm triangle paper.
The path from A to B has already been written.

RT 30   FD 2 _____

_____

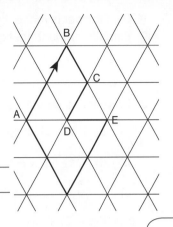

5. Solve these equations.

/3

a) $2n - 4 = n + 5$ $n =$ _____

b) $5(n + 4) = 2(n + 16)$ $n =$ _____

/3

c) $\dfrac{n}{2} + 1 = 4$ $n =$ _____

6. Describe fully the transformation that takes the first shape onto the second shape.
All the shapes are identical.

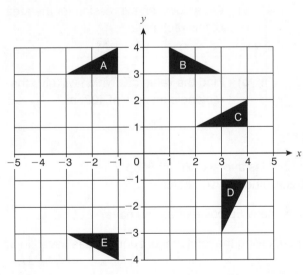

You may find tracing the shape
onto tracing paper useful.

a) A to B

_____

b) B to D

_____

c) A to C

_____

d) B to E

_____

e) E to A

_____

/5

7. Write these numbers in order, smallest first.

 $\dfrac{7}{10}$ 0.45 $\dfrac{4}{5}$ 0.68 $33\frac{1}{3}$ 6% $\dfrac{3}{5}$ $12\frac{1}{2}\%$

/1

_____

8. Gunpowder is made, by weight, from 75% nitre, 15% charcoal and 10% sulphur. Find the amount of each substance in 4 kg of gunpowder.

nitre _____ g   charcoal _____ g   sulphur _____ g   /2

9. Solve these equations.

a) $4x + 7 = 2x + 12$ $x =$ _____

b) $5x = 12$ $x =$ _____

c) $3 = \dfrac{18}{x}$ $x =$ _____

d) $4(x + 3) + 3(x - 4) = 21$ $x =$ _____   /4

10. Amy makes gold hoop earrings. She does this by using gold wire to make circular loops.
The gold wire she uses costs £60 a metre.
The radius of the hoops she makes from the gold wire is 2 cm.
How much will the gold cost to make one of these hoops?

(Take $\pi = 3.1$)   £ _____   /1

11.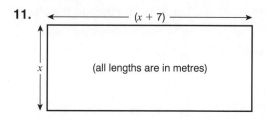

$(x + 7)$

x (all lengths are in metres)

a)   Write down an expression for the area of this rectangle.

_____

b)   Find the value of x which will give the rectangle an area of 408 m².

_____   /2

12. Jordan saves 5p and 10p coins. She has a total of £5 (or 500p).
She has 3 times as many 5p coins as she has 10p coins.

a)   If Jordan has n 10p coins, how many 5p coins does she have? _____

b)   Write an expression involving n, giving the total amount Jordan has saved in 5p and 10p coins. _____

c)   Form and solve an equation to find how many 5p and 10p coins Jordan has.

_____ 5p coins   _____ 10p coins   /3

13. These are the six different types of straight line graph.
Match each of the equations to one of them.

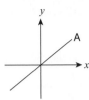

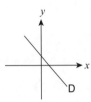 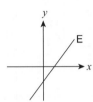 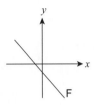

$y = 2x$ _____

$y = 2x + 5$ _____

$y = 3x - 1$ _____

$y = -x$ _____

$y = -2x - 3$ _____

/3

14. Complete the calculations using only these numbers:

| 1 | 2 | 6 | 9 |

a) $\frac{2}{3}$ × _____ = _____

b) _____ ÷ $\frac{1}{3}$ = _____

c) $\frac{1}{3}$ × _____ = _____

d) _____ ÷ $\frac{2}{3}$ = _____

/4

/40

PAPER 16

1. This distance–time graph shows Sarah's motorway journey. At one point she was held up by roadworks.

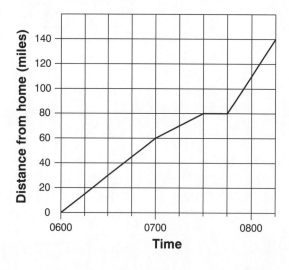

a) At what time did Sarah meet the roadworks? _____

b) How long did Sarah stop for?

_____

c) How long was her journey?

_____ miles

/3

2. a) Write a percentage that is greater than $\frac{8}{10}$ and less than 0.9. _____ %

b) Write a decimal that is greater than 26% and less than 30%. _____

/2

3. For a raffle prize Amy makes up a fruit box.
It contains: $1\frac{1}{2}$ pounds of bananas, 1 pound of apples, $\frac{3}{4}$ pound of grapes and $\frac{1}{4}$ pound of kiwi fruit.
The total weight of the fruit and basket is $4\frac{1}{4}$ pounds.

How much does the basket weigh? _____ pounds

/1

4. Electrum is a metal made from gold and silver. It was used to make the first coins. Electrum is made by mixing gold and silver in the ratio 11 : 9 by weight.

Mixture	Gold	Silver
A	33 g	27 g
B	18 g	22 g
C	5.5 g	1.5 g
D	1.1 g	1.0 g

a) What weight of gold is there in a 20 g electrum coin? _____ g

b) What percentage of the 20 g coin's weight is gold? _____ %

c) Which of the mixtures in the table will make electrum? _____

/3

5. ABCD is a rectangle. Find the angles marked with letters.

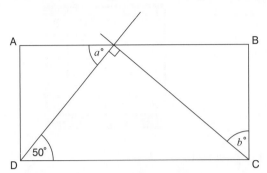

$a = $ _____°

$b = $ _____°

/2

6. Which of these eight angles could be angles of the vertices of a parallelogram?

145°   35°   65°   125°   125°   65°   35°   145°

/1

_____   _____   _____   _____

7. Name the quadrilateral(s) that fit each of these lists of properties.

a) Pairs of opposite angles equal.   _____

b) At least one pair of adjacent sides equal.   _____

c) Just one pair of opposite angles equal.   _____

/3

8. Here are some nets. Which of them fold to make cubes? _____

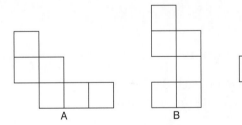
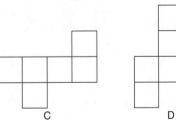

/1

9. Here are two types of commands for moving a model turtle.

FD 10 means move forward 10 cm   **RT 30 means turn 30° clockwise**

The turtle always starts pointing up the page.

a) On a separate piece of centimetre square paper, draw the shape produced by this piece of code (set of instructions).

FD 5   RT 90   FD 4   RT 90   FD 5   RT 90   FD 4

b) Write a piece of code that will produce a square of side 3 cm.

/2

_____

10. Sue started to solve the equation $x^3 + x^2 = 49$ using trial and improvement and a spreadsheet.

Then the computer crashed!
Continue Sue's working to find a solution to 1 d.p.

_____

◇	A	B
1	x	x^3+x^2
2	1	2
3	2	12
4	3	36
5	4	80
6	5	150
7	6	252
8		

/2

11. Put these deals in order of sale price, cheapest first.

    A 10% off £161   **B** 12% off £156   **C** 15% off £153   **D** 20% off £175

_____   _____   _____   _____

/2

12. Two, fair 4-sided, 1 to 4 dice are thrown.

		second dice			
	×	1	2	3	4
first dice 1					
2					
3					
4					

    a) Complete the table showing all the possible scores when the numbers coming up on each dice are multiplied.

    b) What is the most likely score? _____

    c) What is the probability of getting a score of 12? _____

    d) The rule is altered so that the numbers on each dice are added.
    How many different scores are now possible? List them all. _____

/4

13. Amy works for $2\frac{1}{4}$ hours a day as a lunch-time cashier at a building society.
She does this 5 days a week.

    a) How many hours a week does she work? _____ hours

    b) Amy earns £90 a week. How much is she paid an hour? £ _____

/2

14. Solve these equations.

    a) $4x + 3 = 2x + 17$ $x =$ _____

    b) $\dfrac{x}{5} = 30$ $x =$ _____

    c) $3(x + 4) = 2(x + 9)$ $x =$ _____

/3

15.

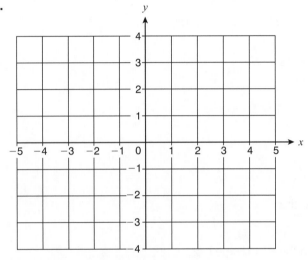

    a) Draw an L, ABC, where A $(-2, 0)$, B$(-2, -1)$ and C $(-1, -1)$.

    b) Draw a x 2 enlargement of ABC with centre of enlargement $(-5, -3)$.

/2

16. This is an unfinished drawing of a cuboid.
It is made up of centimetre cubes.
A 1 cm cube is drawn in grey beside it.

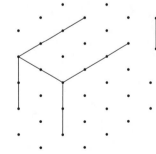

    a) Complete the drawing of the cuboid.

    b) What is the volume of the cuboid?

        _____ cm³

    c) What is the surface area of the cuboid?

        _____ cm²

/3

17. Toni has made a circular coffee table of radius 60 cm.

    a) She wants to buy an adhesive strip to go round the edge.
        What length should she buy?
        Remember to use the correct units.

        (Take π = 3.1) _____ m

    b) She may want to varnish the circular table top.

        What is the area of the table top? _____ m²

18. These triangles are made from rods.
    The pattern of triangles continues.

  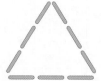

    a) How many rods are there in the
        next (4th) triangle? _____

    b) How many rods are there in the nth triangle? _____

/2

/40

PAPER 17

1. Two friends, Jason and Safiq, want to divide up a collection of 60 posters. Safiq is to get twice as many as Jason. How many should each get?

   Jason _____   Safiq _____

   /1

2. This triangle is drawn on a centimetre squared grid. Calculate the area of the triangle ABC.

   _____ cm²

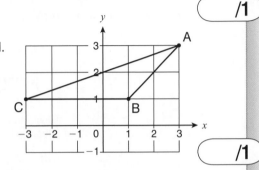

   /1

3. 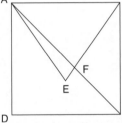   ABCD is a square and ABE is an equilateral triangle. Find the size of:

   a) Angle AFB = _____°

   b) Angle EAF = _____°

   /2

4. A cubic metre of water weighs 1000 kg.

   a) What is the total weight of a full waterbed mattress that is 2 metres by 3 metres by 20 cm if the actual mattress weighs 20 kg? _____ kg

   b) A tonne is 1000 kg. What is the answer to a) in tonnes? _____ tonnes

   /2

5. This arrow has one line of symmetry.

   a) Write down a formula for the perimeter, P, of the shape. _____

   b) Find the value of x which will give the arrow a perimeter of 77 metres. _____ m

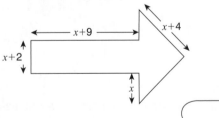

   /3

6. This pie chart shows how Amy spends her weekly earnings.

a) She spends £120 a week on rent.

How much does she spend a week on travel? £ _____

b) How much does Amy save a week? £ _____

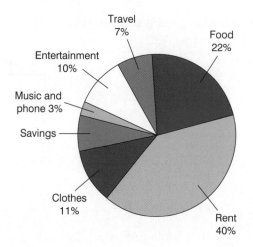

Travel
7%

Food
22%

Entertainment
10%

Music and
phone 3%

Savings

Clothes
11%

Rent
40%

/2

7. This solid is made from eight cubes.
Match each of the views in the box, with one of the viewing directions A, B, C, D or E.

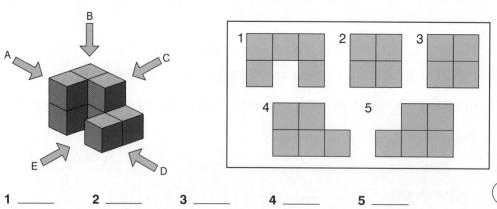

B

A

C

E

D

1

2

3

4

5

1 _____   **2** _____   **3** _____   **4** _____   **5** _____

/2

8. An unusual die has six faces labelled 1, 2, 3, 5, 7 and 9. If two of these dice are rolled, and the numbers showing on the upper faces are added, what is the number of possible different answers and what are they?

/2

9. Which of these straight lines are parallel to each other?

1 $y = 2$ **2** $y = 2x + 2$ **3** $y = 2x$ **4** $y = x + 2$ **5** $x = 20$

 /1

10. According to the label on a pair of jeans they will shrink by 4% when they are first washed.

By what fraction will they have shrunk? _____

 /1

11. a) A sequence has this term-to-term rule: add two to the previous term

The first term is 3. Write down the first four terms of the sequence.

_____   _____   _____   _____

b) Write down an expression for the nth term of the sequence above.

$T(n) =$ _____

 /2

12. Calculate the area of this logo.
The logo is made from semi-circles.
Take π to be 3.

_____ cm^2

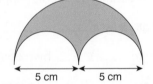

5 cm   5 cm

 /1

13. Find the sixth angle of an irregular hexagon when the other angles are 100°, 120°,

125°, 120° and 130°. _____ °

 /1

14. The price of a house went up by 200% between 1985 and 1995.
In 1985 it was worth £50000. Jean says that the house price has doubled in this time.
Is she correct and why?

_____ because _____

/1

15. The black line is the path traced by a turtle
carrying out this line of coding.
(The turtle begins at O facing up the page.)

FD 2   LT 90   FD 1   LT 90   FD 4

The turtle continues its journey to return to
O shown by the grey line.
Continue the coding to show the return
journey.

_____

_____

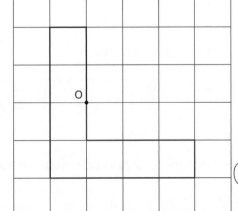

/2

16. Jake takes the temperature every day at noon for a week. The mean for the first 6 days is 1 °C. The mean temperature for the week was 0 °C.

What was the temperature on the last day? _____°C

17. Heavy 10-pin bowling balls weigh $6\frac{1}{4}$ kg.

a) What will six of these balls weigh? _____ kg

b) How many of these heavy 10-pin bowling balls will it take to weigh a tonne (1000 kg)?

_____

/2

18. Solve these equations.

a) $5x - 2 = 3x + 4$ $x =$ _____

b) $4(3y + 10) = 9y + 64$ $x =$ _____

c) $\frac{1}{2}x + 3 = 21$ $x =$ _____

/3

19. Complete these sentences about mapping triangles 1, 2, 3, etc.

a) 1 maps onto 2 by a _____

b) 2 maps onto _____ by a quarter clockwise turn about the origin.

c) 2 maps onto _____ by a translation of 1 unit to the right and 8 units down.

d) 7 maps onto 6 by a _____

e) 2 maps onto 7 by a

_____

f) A _____

maps 7 onto 4

g) 8 maps onto 5 by a

_____

h) 4 maps onto 7 by a

_____

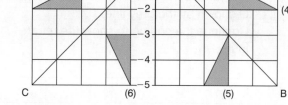

/4

20.

◇	A	B
1	x	x^2-19
2	3	−10
3	4	3
4	5	6
5	4.1	
6	4.5	1.25
7	4.2	
8	4.3	−0.51
9	4.4	0.36
10	4.35	
11	4.36	0.0096
12	4.37	0.0969
13		
14		

The equation $x^2 - 19 = 0$ has a solution between 4 and 5.
Complete the missing cells in this spreadsheet.
Find the solution correct to 1 decimal place.

$x =$ _____

/2

21. When three fair 6-sided dice are thrown the probability of getting 3 sixes is 0.5%.

What is the probability of not getting 3 sixes? _____%

/1

22. Complete this magic square.

1	—	$\dfrac{19}{20}$
—	$\dfrac{3}{4}$	$\dfrac{4}{5}$
$\dfrac{11}{20}$	—	$\dfrac{1}{2}$

/3

/40

PAPER 18

1. The angles of a triangle are in the ratio 5 : 2 : 2.
What are the angles and what is the name of this type of triangle?

_____°   _____°   _____°

/2

2. Solve these equations.

a) $5x - 2 = 3x + 4$ $x =$ _____

b) $2(x - 5) = x + 2$ $x =$ _____

/2

3. Calculate the length of this piece of wire.
All the curved sections are semi-circles.

(Take $\pi = 3.1$)

_____ cm

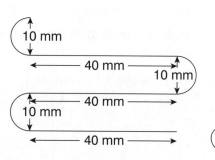

/2

4. Find the sizes of the angles marked with letters.

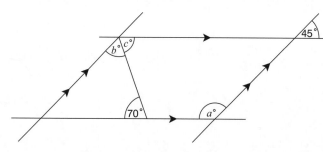

$a =$ _____°

$b =$ _____°

$c =$ _____°

/3

5. Write down the equations of three straight lines that pass through the point (1, 1)

a) _____

b) _____

c) _____

/1

6. Here are the front, side and plan views of a solid made from four cubes.
Make a drawing of the solid on this triangle isometric paper.

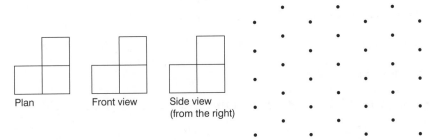

Plan   Front view   Side view
(from the right)

/1

7. This is a sequence involving fractions: $\frac{1}{2}$ $\frac{2}{3}$ $\frac{3}{4}$ $\frac{4}{5}$ ...

a) Write the next two terms.

_____   _____

b) Write an expression for the nth term. $T(n) =$ _____

/2

8. How many $2\frac{1}{4}$ cm lengths of wire can be cut from 36 cm of wire? _____

/1

9. The three sides of a triangle, in centimetres, are $(2x + 3)$, $(x + 13)$ and $(x + 4)$.

a) Find a value of x so the triangle is isosceles. _____

b) For what value of x will the triangle have a perimeter of 40 cm? _____

/2

10. The maximum distance, d, a motorcycle stunt driver can safely jump horizontally
at a particular speed depends on the height of the ramp, h.

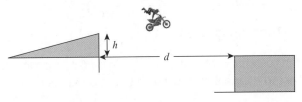

For a particular speed the formula is $h = 0.004d^2 - 0.09d$
All distances are in metres.

Use trial and improvement to find what distance, to the nearest metre, can be

jumped using a ramp height of 2 m. _____ m

/1

11. This distance–time graph shows a race between Amber and Jade over two lengths of a swimming pool.

   a) What was one length of the pool? _____ m

   b) Who won the race? _____

   c) Who swam the first length faster? _____

   d) Who rested after the first length and for how long? _____

   for _____ seconds

/4

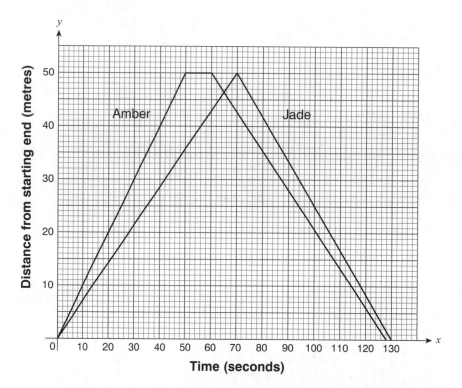

12. All the rain water falling on a rectangular flat roof measuring 12 m by 8 m is collected. How many litres of water are collected after a storm in which 9 mm of rain fell?

_____

/2

13. Write these in order, smallest first.

   $\frac{3}{7}$ 37%   0.4   42% $\frac{3}{8}$ 0.43

_____

/1

14. Find the values of the distances indicated by letters.
All distances are measured in inches.

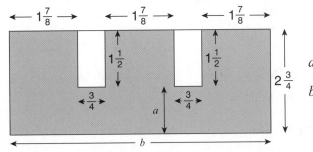

$a =$ _____ inches

$b =$ _____ inches

/2

15. Calculate the area of this tile.

_____

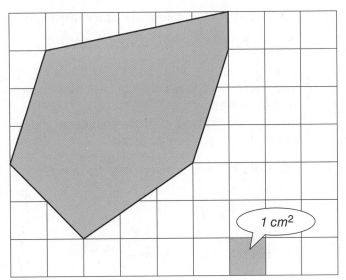

1 cm²

/2

16. This 5-pointed star has rotational symmetry of order 5.
Calculate the values of the angles shown by letters.

$a =$ _____

$b =$ _____

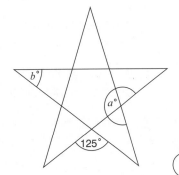

$b°$

$a°$

125°

/2

17. Here are four commands for a model turtle.

FD 10 means move forward 10 cm
RT 30 means turn 30° clockwise
LIFT means the turtle's pen will not draw
a line when it moves
DROP puts the turtle's pen down to draw

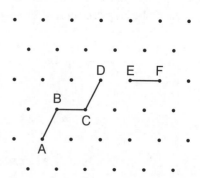

Starting from A write the commands to draw
this route:
A to B to C to D then on from E to F on 1 cm
triangle paper.

The code for A to B has already been written:

RT 30   FD 1 _____

/2

18. Anita wonders if people tend to have best friends who are about the same height
as themselves.
She collects the heights of some students and their best friends' heights. She plots this
information onto a scatter graph.

a) Does the tallest person have the tallest
friend? _____
What are the two heights?

tallest person _____ cm

tallest friend _____ cm

b) Does the shortest person have the
shortest friend? _____
What are the two heights?

shortest person _____ cm

shortest friend _____ cm

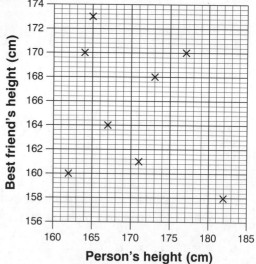

c) What correlation is there between a
person's height and that of their best friend?

_____

/3

19.

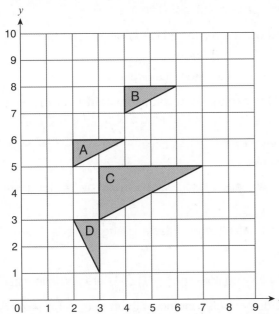

Describe fully the transformation that maps:

a) A onto B

_____

b) A onto D

_____

c) A onto C

_____

/3

20. Which of these points are above, on, or below the line $y = 2x - 1$?

A(-4, -1)   B(0, -1)   C(5, 1)   D(3, 5)   E(0, 0)   F(5, 8)   G(1, 2)

Above _____   On _____   Below _____

/2

/40

area	the amount of space inside a 2-D shape
arrowhead	a quadrilateral which has one inside angle greater than 180° and one line of symmetry
circumference	the distance around the edge of a circle
correlation	a measure of the strength of relationship between two sets of data – how close they are to forming a straight-line graph
diameter	the distance from one side of a circle to another which passes through the centre
equation	an equation is two equal expressions linked by '=', for example $2x + 1 = 11$
equilateral triangle	a triangle which has all three sides and angles equal
equivalent	having the same value, for example $\frac{1}{2}$, $\frac{2}{4}$, $\frac{10}{20}$ are equivalent fractions.
expression	numbers and/or symbols together with an operator/operators $(+, -, \times)$. e.g. $7 + 3$; $4x - 1$; $x^2 + y^2$; $2a + 6 + 5b$
frequency table	a table for a set of observations showing how frequently each event or quantity occurs.
hexagon	a six-sided polygon
intersect	cross over, for example these three lines intersect at P
isosceles triangle	a triangle with two equal sides (and two equal angles)
mean	the average of a set of numbers calculated by adding the numbers then dividing by how many numbers there are
median	the middle number in a set of numbers which are arranged according to size, the median of 1 3 6 7 9 is 6, the median of 2 4 6 10 is 5 $((4 + 6) \div 10)$
midpoint	the point halfway along a line
mode	an average which is the number that occurs most often in a set of numbers
net	a 2-D shape that can be cut around and folded to make a 3-D shape, for example, one net for a cube is:
origin	the point (0, 0) on a graph where the x and y axes cross

parallel	two lines are parallel if they are the same distance apart all along their length and never touch or intersect
parallelogram	a four sided shape which has opposite sides parallel and of the same length and with equal opposite angles (this includes squares, rectangles and rhombuses)
pentagon	a five sided polygon (2-D shape)
perimeter	the distance around the edges of a 2-D shape
pie chart	a circular chart divided into sectors representing relative amounts
prime number	a number which can only be divided by 1 and itself without a remainder, 2, 3, 5, 7, 11, and 13 are all prime numbers
probability	how likely it is that something will happen
product	the outcome of two or more numbers when multiplied together, so the product of 3 and 4 is 3 × 4 = 12.
quadrilateral	a 2-D shape with 4 sides
radius	the distance between any point on a circle's edge and its centre point
range	the difference between the highest and lowest values of a set of data
ratio	a ratio shows the relative sizes of two or more values separated by ':' For example, the ratio of gold to silver in a coin is 2 : 7
regular polygon	a polygon that has all its sides equal and all its angles equal
rhombus	a four-sided shape with all sides of equal length
scatter graph	a graph of plotted points that show the relationship between two sets of data
sequence	a list of numbers placed in a particular order, with a rule linking terms, for example: 1, 3, 5, 7, ... or 3, 9, 27, 81, ...
surface area	the sum of the areas of each 2-D face of a 3-D shape
translation	moving a shape to a different position but keeping the same line lengths and angle values
trapezium	a quadrilateral with just one pair of parallel sides
vertex/vertices	a point where two or more straight lines meet (a corner) These lettered points are vertices
volume	the amount of space a 3-D shape fills

Progress grid

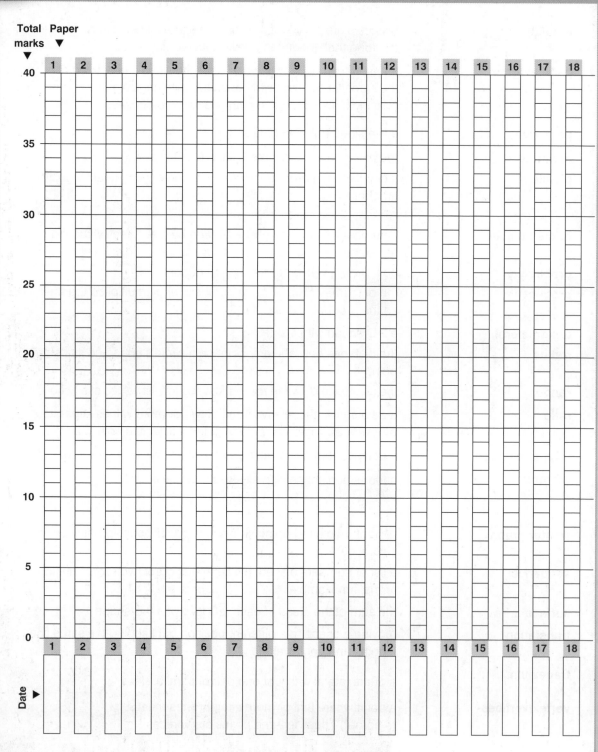

Now colour in your score!